CALCULUS IN
5 HOURS

CONCEPTS REVEALED SO YOU DON'T HAVE TO SIT THROUGH A SEMESTER OF LECTURES

DENNIS JARECKE

D1554378

Calculus In 5 Hours: Concepts Revealed so You Don't Have to Sit Through a Semester of Lectures
by Dennis Jarecke

Published by Six Sycamores, LLC
14949 Lakewood Heights Boulevard, Lakewood, Ohio 44107

www.CalculusSolution.com

ISBN: 978-0-9995254-1-8

Preface

Calculus is a vast and detailed subject that can take a lifetime to learn. So to teach Calculus in five hours I need to cut out a lot of material.

This book covers approximately 75% of the material taught in a college Calculus 1 course. Most of what's been cut out are function limits and trigonometric functions.

So why should you read this book?

Because you can learn the basics of Calculus quickly. Learning comes down to repetition. The more you're exposed to Calculus and the more familiar it becomes, the more likely you are to understand it.

By learning Calculus in five hours, you cram almost a semester's worth of material in your head quickly. When you cover it in your actual course, you'll be exposed to it a *second* time which allows you to learn it easier and faster at that point.

A second reason for reading this book is for a review. You may have learned Calculus years ago, but have forgotten it. Now you need or want to relearn it.

If this sounds like you, then this book will let you accomplish that. I don't assume you know Calculus. Instead, I take you from knowing nothing to having a broad overview of the main tools and concepts that are typically learned over the course of a college semester. And given your previous knowledge of Calculus, this will facilitate a quick relearning of the subject.

This book is organized into five parts and 32 chapters. The amount of time to go through each chapter is given in the table of contents and at the beginning of each part and chapter.

If this is your first time learning Calculus, go through the book sequentially to make sure you understand the concepts. If you're learning Calculus for the second time, feel free to skip around to get what you need.

And then when you're ready, head over to **www.CalculusSolution.com** for more lessons, Calculus specific calculators, and a library of fully worked out problems so you can get ahead with less effort.

For my wife and children,
Susan, Sara, Emily, Kiera, and Michael,
who put up with me sitting in the basement doing
Calculus stuff.
I love you all very much.

To Dave Van Horn,
who understands the starts, stops, and frustrations of
getting something done. Thanks for listening, answering
questions, and being a big help to writers and
entrepreneurs in the Cleveland area.

Special thanks to all those teachers and professors who
had a hand in teaching me Calculus. I hope you know
there are students who think what you do is really cool. I
was one of them.
Thanks for making Calculus come alive.

Table of Contents

Your Biggest Obstacle to Learning Calculus

The obvious goal of this book is to teach you Calculus and to teach it to you quickly. However, there's one problem I can't overcome in this book.

Most people have been brainwashed into thinking they're bad at math. This brainwashing comes from experiences in school, upbringing, peer pressure, and a popular culture that often portrays smart people as anti-social and weird.

You may feel you can't learn something as complex as Calculus, but the scientific research doesn't support this.

You were born with an ability to learn, discover, and become an expert at mathematics. Learning a language is harder than learning Calculus. The only difference is that you don't remember how difficult it was to learn to speak, read, and write English. Yet, you accomplished it, didn't you?

The reason you were able to do something so complex at a young age is because you were born with a massively powerful supercomputer in your head. This supercomputer is deep inside your brain, and it specializes in detecting and amplifying patterns, performing mathematical operations, learning new concepts, and coming up with ideas from thin air.

But surrounding your supercomputer is a filter that limits what goes in and what comes out. That filter is your *self-image*.

If your self-image is programmed to believe you're not good at math, then you'll never demonstrate a proficiency in mathematics. However, if your self-image is changed so you know you're good at mathematics, then you'll be successful at learning it.

This isn't a bunch of cheerleading psycho-babble. A person who believes they're bad at math can be hypnotized and convinced they're good at it. In a state of hypnosis they can accurately work out math problems they've been exposed to, but consciously thought they couldn't solve.

Specifically, math avoidant college students have been exposed to hypnotic techniques and compared to control groups of similar college students. By using well-documented techniques of Ericksonian hypnotherapy, math instructors are able to systematically modify students' beliefs about their ability to do mathematics. Once their beliefs have been changed, those students make more A's, B's, and C's than those students in the control group.

In other words, a person's self-image can be changed to make them believe they're good at math. This allows their supercomputer to accept mathematical instructions, do the calculations, and give the correct answer.

To be clear, hypnosis by itself won't magically give you mathematical abilities. It can only modify your conscious and artificially negative belief that you're bad at math. Mathematical training (at whatever level you desire or need to be good at) plus a positive belief in your ability to do math is what creates success.

In the absence of hypnosis, you can associate positive emotions with learning Calculus. Think of a time you accomplished something you were proud of. Now take that same feeling and imagine getting the highest grade you've ever gotten in a math class.

This will start the process of changing your self-image. And when you do make a higher grade, your self-image will have been reprogrammed to believe you're good at math.

So, learning Calculus is not a matter of "if." It's a matter of "when."

In this book I promise to teach you Calculus as fast as I know how. Your job is to believe the scientific research and experience of people just like you who were able to learn Calculus.

You have a powerful computer in your head, and it will let you learn Calculus if you put positive, successful emotions into your learning process.

Let's begin . . .

Part 1 - Functions and an Overview of Calculus (27 minutes)

In part one there are four chapters. In it I'll introduce functions, what we can do with them, and then introduce the two main types of Calculus: Differential Calculus and Integral Calculus.

Chapter 1: Functions (10 minutes)

Calculus deals with functions, so knowing what they are is important. You've already seen them in High School, but it never hurts to go over them again.

A function is a way of assigning one set of numbers to another set of numbers.

For example, let's say you're at home and start walking through town. As you walk you keep track of how far you are from your house, and you measure the height of the buildings as you go. (Let's say you measure the height of the buildings on your right-hand side.) At every distance from your home, there is a height of a building. This is a function, and it may look something like this:

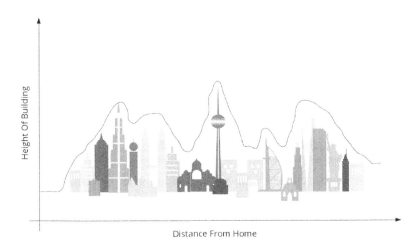

If you want to describe your function like a mathematician would, label the horizontal axis the "x-axis," the vertical axis the "y-axis," and the function as "f(x)." A typical function looks something like:

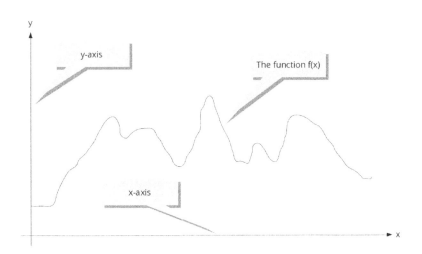

In Calculus you describe functions in a way that is precise and allows you to do more advanced things with them. A rigorous definition of a function has four components:

1) A rule relating the x-axis with the y-axis.

Typically this is an algebraic, trigonometric or other relationship such as $\sin(x)$, $\ln(x)$, x^2, or $x^3 + 2x - 5$.

When writing down a function, you denote it as $f(x)$ or sometimes by y. For example, you would denote the function x^2 as $y = x^2$ or as $f(x) = x^2$.

2) For every value of x there is only one value of y.

In other words, you can't have two buildings on the same spot. This means $y = x^2$ is a function, but $y = \sqrt{x}$ is not. Why?

Let's find the value of x^2 and $\sqrt{x}$ at $x = 4$. For the function $y = x^2$, $y = 16$ at $x = 4$. However, for $y = \sqrt{x}$, y can be either +2 or -2 at $x = 4$. At $x = 4$ there are two possible values of y for the function $y = \sqrt{x}$, but only one value for y for the function $y = x^2$. In other words, $\sqrt{x}$ is ambiguous between two possible numbers, and x^2 is not. That's why x^2 is a function and $\sqrt{x}$ is not.

Pictorially, this is a function:

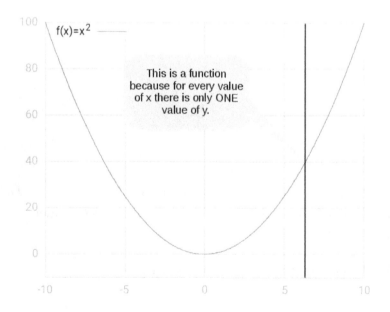

And this is not a function:

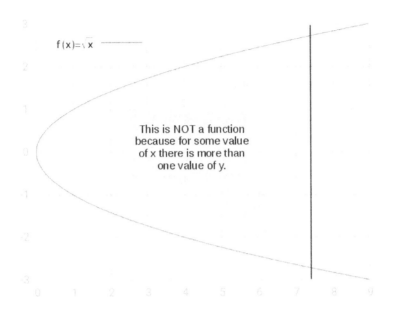

f(x)=√x

This is NOT a function because for some value of x there is more than one value of y.

If we wrote $y = |\sqrt{x}|$ or $y = -|\sqrt{x}|$ where $||$ denotes the absolute value, then these would be functions because y has only one value for every value of x. This fact is so well known that you rarely see $f(x) = |\sqrt{x}|$. You usually see $f(x) = \sqrt{x}$ which should always be taken to mean $f(x) = |\sqrt{x}|$. Similarly, $f(x) = -\sqrt{x}$ means $f(x) = -|\sqrt{x}|$.

3) The <u>domain</u> of the function is the portion of the x-axis for which the function is defined.

When I say the word "defined," I mean that $f(x)$ is a known number. If I know that $f(2) = 17$, then the function is defined at $x = 2$. If I don't know the value of $f(x)$ at $x = 2$, then the function is undefined there.

Whenever the domain is not specified, you assume the domain is all real numbers for which $f(x)$ is a real number. For example, for $f(x) = x^2$ the domain is all real numbers.

However, for $f(x) = |\sqrt{x}|$ the domain is all positive numbers because the square root of a negative number is not a real number. It's an imaginary number.

When you need to explicitly define the domain of a function, you do it with a bracket that dictates what rule relating the x and y axes is used for which part of the domain. For example,

$$f(x) = \begin{cases} 2x + 5, & 5 \leq x \leq 10 \\ x^2, & -2 < x < 3 \\ x^8 - 5x^4 - 7, & x < -3 \end{cases}$$

denotes a function whose domain is not made up of all real numbers. The domain is $(-\infty, -3) \cup (-2, 3) \cup [5, 10]$ where $\cup$ is the *union* of the three intervals $(-\infty, -3)$, $(-2, 3)$, and $[5, 10]$.

Oh yeah, an interval is a way of saying all numbers between two points on the x-axis. So $[5, 10]$ is a fancy math way of saying all the numbers between 5 and 10. The difference between parentheses and brackets is that for parentheses the point is not included, but for brackets it is. So -3 is not included in the interval $(-\infty, -3)$, but all points less than it are. The numbers 5 and 10 are included in the interval $[5, 10]$. And you can have mixed intervals like $(3, 20]$ which includes the number 20, but not the number 3.

4) The <u>range</u> of the function is the portion of the y-axis for which the function is defined.

The range is determined by knowing the domain and the rule relating the x-axis with the y-axis.

Here are five examples of the domain, range, and graph of a function:

Function $f(x) = x^2$

Domain (x-axis): All real numbers. In math notation you write: $(-\infty, \infty)$

Range (y-axis): All positive real numbers. In math notation you write: $[0, \infty)$

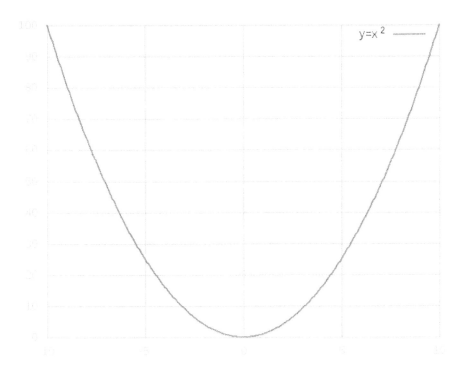

Function $f(x) = x^3$

Domain (x-axis): All real numbers. In math notation you write: $(-\infty, \infty)$

Range (y-axis): All real numbers. In math notation you write: $(-\infty, \infty)$

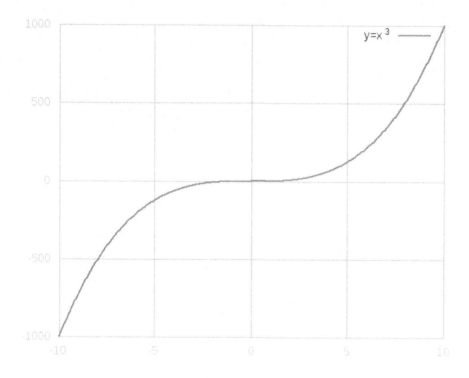

Function $f(x) = -\sqrt{x}$

Domain (x-axis): All positive real numbers. In math notation you write: $[0, \infty)$

Range (y-axis): All negative real numbers. In math notation you write: $(-\infty, 0]$

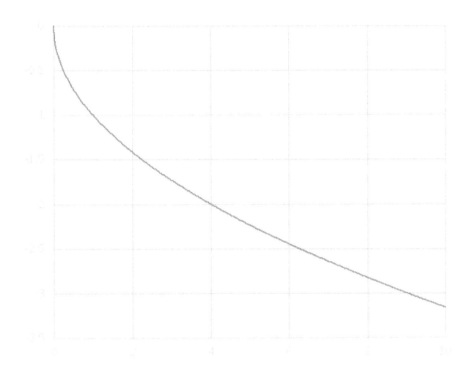

Function $f(x) = \sin(x)$

Domain (x-axis): All real numbers. In math notation you write: $(-\infty, \infty)$

Range (y-axis): All real numbers between -1 and 1. In math notation you write: $[-1, 1]$

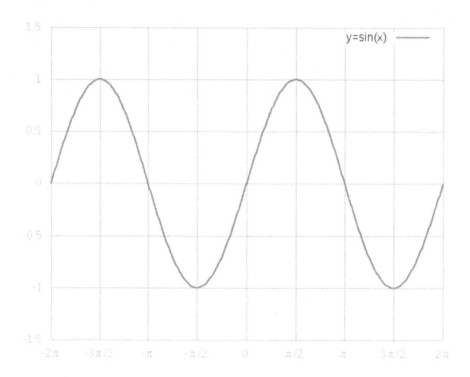

Function $f(x) = \begin{cases} x^2, & x \geq 2 \\ x^3, & x < -3 \end{cases}$

Domain (x-axis): All real numbers between minus infinity and negative 3 (but not including negative three), AND all real numbers between positive 2 and positive infinity. In math notation you write: $(-\infty, -3) \cup [2, \infty)$

Range (y-axis): All real numbers between negative infinity and negative 27, AND all real numbers between positive 4 and positive infinity. In math notation you write: $(-\infty, -27) \cup [4, \infty)$

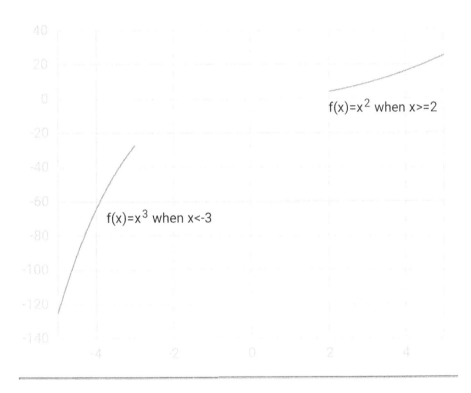

Now that you know what a function is and have seen some examples, let's talk about two important classes of functions: straight lines and polynomials.

Chapter 2: Straight Lines and Polynomials (7 minutes)

To understand Calculus you must first understand two types of important functions: **straight lines** and **polynomials**.

As you'll see in a minute, a straight line is a polynomial, but it's important to understand a straight line first because it's the basis for understanding Differential Calculus.

You've seen straight lines since the day you were born, but to understand them fully you must know the two fundamental characteristics of every straight line: **slope** and **y-intercept**.

The formula for a straight line is typically denoted by

$$y = mx + b$$

where m is the slope and b is the y-intercept.

The slope (m) is a measure of how "steep" the line is, and the y-intercept is where the line hits the y-axis. (By the way, you should memorize the last sentence.) See the next page for a picture of the slope and y-intercept.

Slope is a very important concept. It's defined as how much the straight line "rises" divided by the amount it "runs." So the larger the slope the "steeper" the line is.

When the slope is a positive number, it goes up ("rises") as the line "runs" from left to right. When the slope is negative, it goes down ("falls") as the line "runs" from left to right.

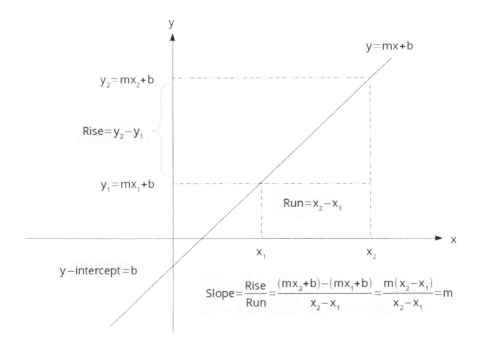

A broader class of functions is that of polynomials. A polynomial is a function of the form

$$f(x) = a_n x^n + a_{n-1} x^{n-1} + \cdots + a_1 x + a_0,$$

where n is a positive integer. The variables $a_0, a_1, \ldots, a_n$ are numbers.

Here are four examples of polynomials:

- The straight line, $f(x) = m\,x + b$.
- $f(x) = 4x^2 - 7$
- $f(x) = 200\,x^7 - 1.5\,x^5 + 6\,x^2$
- $f(x) = (2x - a)(5x + b)$

And here are some functions that are not polynomials:

- $f(x) = 1/x$
- $f(x) = \ln(x)$ (The natural logarithm discussed in Chapter 31.)
- $f(x) = e^x$ (The exponential function discussed in Chapter 31.)

- Trigonometric functions like $\sin(x)$ and $\cos(x)$.

There are several terms associated with polynomials that are important to know:

- The $a_n, a_{n-1}, \cdots, a_1$ and a_0 are called **coefficients**.
- a_n is called the **leading coefficient**.
- The **degree** of the polynomial is the highest integer for which a_n is not zero.

For the four polynomial examples on the previous page, let's find the degree and leading coefficient of each:

Function	Leading Coefficient	Degree
$f(x) = mx + b$	m	1
$f(x) = 4x^2 - 7$	4	2
$f(x) = 200\,x^7 - 1.5\,x^5 + 6\,x^2$	200	7
$f(x) = (2x - 3)(5x + 6)$	10	2

For the last function,

$$(2x - 3)(5x + 6) = 10x^2 - 3x - 18.$$

Only by expanding it can you determine the leading coefficient and degree.

Exercise: Go to www.CalculusSolution.com/Calculus-Calculator and graph the polynomials above.

In the next chapter I'll show you five different ways you can combine two functions. Pay close attention to function composition because that's the one you might not be familiar with.

Chapter 3: Combining Functions (7 minutes)

You can combine functions in different ways to create other functions. You can add, subtract, multiply, and divide two functions to create a new function. You did this in High School, but let's do some examples anyway.

Adding two functions: Let's add

$$f(x) = 4x^3 + 2x^2 - 5x + 8$$

and

$$g(x) = 1.5x^7 + 3x^2 + 4x - 2.$$

To do this you add like terms. For example, group the x^2 terms to get $2x^2 + 3x^2 = 5x^2$. The answer is

$$f(x) + g(x) = 1.5x^7 + 4x^3 + 5x^2 - x + 6.$$

Subtracting two functions: Let's subtract

$$f(x) = 4x^3 + 2x^2 - 5x + 8$$

from

$$g(x) = 1.5x^7 + 3x^2 + 4x - 2.$$

Subtract like terms to get

$$g(x) - f(x) = 1.5x^7 - 4x^3 + x^2 + 9x - 10.$$

Multiply two functions: Let's multiply

$$f(x) = 4x^3 + 2x^2 - 5x + 8$$

and

$$g(x) = 1.5x^7 + 3x^2 + 4x - 2$$

together. Okay, this one is time-consuming, but not hard. We get

$$
\begin{aligned}
g(x) * f(x) \quad = \quad & 6x^{10} + 3x^9 - 7.5x^8 \\
+ \quad & 12x^7 + 12x^5 + 22x^4 \\
- \quad & 15x^3 + 42x - 16
\end{aligned}
$$

Divide two functions: Let's be honest, doing this is hard and not useful in the context of learning Calculus in 5 hours. Let's skip it.

We can also combine two functions by **function composition**. *Function composition is where we put one function inside another function.* For example, we can put a function $g(x)$ inside the function $f(x)$ by doing $f(g(x))$.

Let's do an example.

Let's say that $f(x) = -x - 1$ and $g(x) = -3x^2$. The first step to find $f(g(x))$ is to replace x by g everywhere in $f(x)$ like so:

$$f(g) = -g - 1.$$

Now, everywhere you see g replace it with $-3x^2$ like this:

$$f(g(x)) = - \left[-3x^2 \right] - 1.$$

For the last step, do some algebra to clean things up. You get

$$f(g(x)) = 3x^2 - 1.$$

Exercise: Find $f(g(x))$ where $f(x) = -2x^2 - 4$ and $g(x) = -x$. (The answer is $f(g(x)) = -2x^2 - 4$. Go to www.CalculusSolution.com/node/31550 for the solution.)

Finally, there are three more things you need to know:

- The function composition $f(g(x))$ is typically denoted by mathematicians as $(f \circ g)(x)$.

- The function composition $g(f(x))$ is typically denoted by mathematicians as $(g \circ f)(x)$.
- $(f \circ g)(x)$ is not always equal to $(g \circ f)(x)$.

To prove the last point, find $g(f(x))$ for $f(x)$ and $g(x)$ in the exercise above. (You previously found $f(g(x))$, so now find $g(f(x))$.) The answer is $2x^2 + 4$. (See www.CalculusSolution.com/node/31826 for the solution.)

Therefore, $(f \circ g)(x) \neq (g \circ f)(x)$ for these two particular functions. Occasionally you'll find two functions where $(f \circ g)(x) = (g \circ f)(x)$, but it's not guaranteed to be true in general.

Now that you've spent the last three chapters reviewing functions, it's time to reveal what Calculus is.

Here we go . . .

Chapter 4 - The Two Basic Concepts of Calculus (3 minutes)

Calculus comes in two flavors. The first is **Differential Calculus**, and the second is **Integral Calculus**.

Differential Calculus is where you find the slope of a function at a specific point. Integral Calculus is where you find the area underneath a function.

Let's talk about Differential Calculus first.

In High School you learned the slope of a straight line is the line's "rise" divided by its "run."

However, for any other function, the slope can be different depending on where you look. *Differential Calculus is about finding all the slopes a function can have.*

For example, the picture on the next page shows that the function $f(x) = x^2$ has a slope of -10 at $x = -5$, 0 at $x = 0$, and 4 at $x = 2$. So depending on where you look, the slope will be different.

The way to visualize the slope at a particular point is by <u>drawing a straight line that has the same slope</u> as $f(x)$ at that point and touches $f(x)$ there. This is called a *tangent line,* and it's always used to visually represent the slope of the function at a specific point.

The picture on the next page also shows the tangent lines at $x = -5$, $x = 0$, and $x = 2$. (In Chapter 7 I'll show you the exact formula for the tangent line, so don't worry too much about what it is right now.)

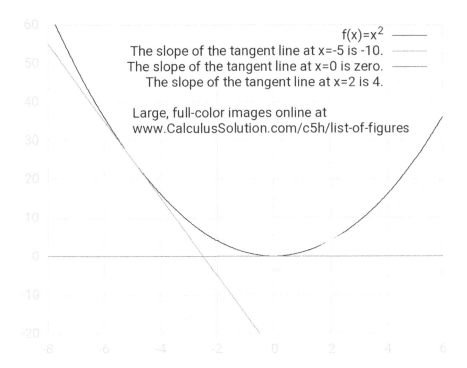

$f(x)=x^2$ ———
The slope of the tangent line at x=-5 is -10. ———
The slope of the tangent line at x=0 is zero. ———
The slope of the tangent line at x=2 is 4.

Large, full-color images online at
www.CalculusSolution.com/c5h/list-of-figures

When dealing with functions that are not straight lines, it's common to stop calling the slope "slope" and start referring to it as a **derivative**. Derivatives are denoted by $f'(x)$ or df/dx. In other words,

$$\text{Slope} = \text{Derivative} = f'(x) = \frac{df}{dx}.$$

The more accurate way to think about it is this. Once you have the derivative, $f'(x)$, you can find the slope at any point on the function by putting into the derivative the value of x where you want to find the slope. For example, if the derivative of $f(x) = x^3$ is $f'(x) = 3x^2$, then you can find the slope at $x = 4$ by plugging 4 into the derivative to get the slope like so:

$$
\begin{aligned}
\text{Slope at 4} \;&=\; f'(4) \\
&=\; 3(4^2) \\
&=\; 3 \cdot 16 \\
&=\; 48.
\end{aligned}
$$

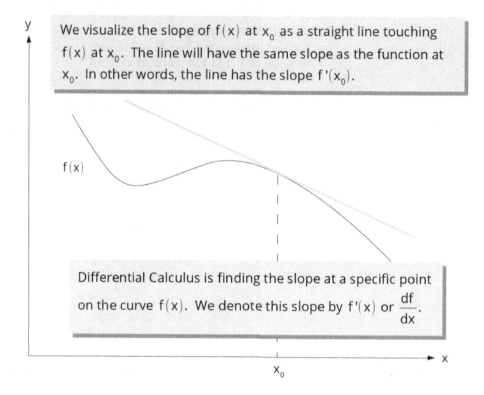

We visualize the slope of $f(x)$ at x_0 as a straight line touching $f(x)$ at x_0. The line will have the same slope as the function at x_0. In other words, the line has the slope $f'(x_0)$.

$f(x)$

Differential Calculus is finding the slope at a specific point on the curve $f(x)$. We denote this slope by $f'(x)$ or $\dfrac{df}{dx}$.

x_0

Now for Integral Calculus.

In High School geometry class you had to learn the area of common shapes like rectangles, circles, squares, and triangles.

Integral Calculus is about finding the area underneath a function. The area under a function is referred to as an **integral**, and it's denoted by

$$\text{Area} = \text{Integral} = \int_a^b f(x)dx,$$

where a and b are the two points on the x-axis between which you find the area. See the picture on the next page.

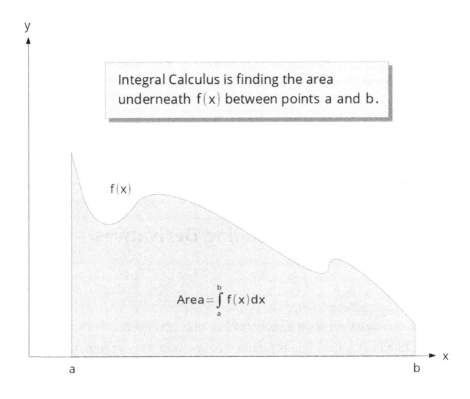

Integral Calculus is finding the area underneath $f(x)$ between points a and b.

$f(x)$

$$\text{Area} = \int_a^b f(x)\,dx$$

Congratulations! You've made it through Part 1. In Part 2 I'm going to go through derivatives and a real-world application.

Onward . . .

Part 2 - Derivatives (127 minutes)

In this part you'll learn about derivatives - what they are, how to get them, and what they're used for.

Chapter 5 - Understanding Derivatives (25 minutes)

$\mathbf{T}$o understand what a derivative is, you first need to know what a **secant line** is. A secant line is pictured below, and it's a straight line that touches the function at (at least) two points.

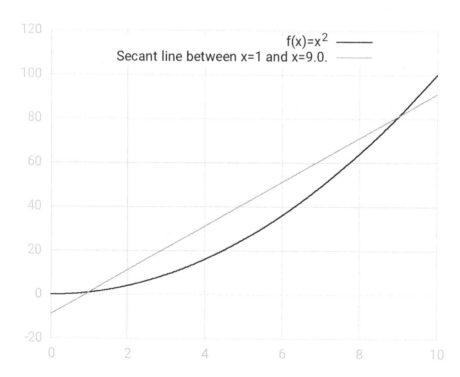

Because it's a straight line it has a slope:

$$\text{Slope} = \frac{\text{Rise}}{\text{Run}} = \frac{9^2 - 1^2}{9 - 1} = 10$$

Suppose you want to know the slope of $f(x) = x^2$ at $x = 1$. You can have more and more secant lines that get closer and closer to $x = 1$, and then calculate the slope of each one. See the picture below.

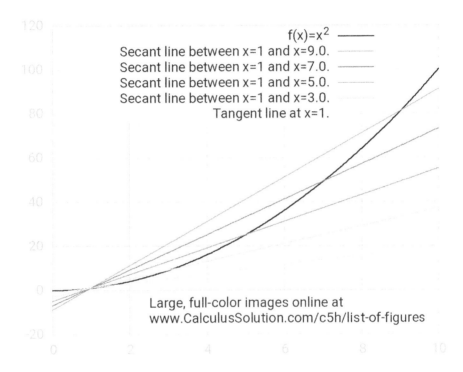

Large, full-color images online at
www.CalculusSolution.com/c5h/list-of-figures

Now, imagine one of those secant lines getting extremely close to $x = 1$ and *almost* touching $f(x)$ at one point. This imagined secant line is called a **tangent line**.

The slope of the tangent line is the slope of the function at that point. We usually stop calling it a slope and start referring to it as a derivative. In other words, a derivative is another word for slope.

Exercise: Calculate the value of the slope for each secant line in the picture on the previous page. (Answers: 10, 8, 6, 4, 2. At $x = 1$ you had to divide by zero, didn't you? But you can't divide by zero so keep reading.)

The use of the Greek "Δ" symbol is common in science, and it means "take the difference" or, equivalently, "the change in."

Let's say you have two variables, a_1 and a_2, and took the difference $a_2 - a_1$. This difference is typically denoted by Δa. In other words, $\Delta a = a_2 - a_1$. In plain English you refer to Δa as "delta a" or "the change in a."

Because rise is defined as $f(x_2) - f(x_1)$ (the change in $f(x)$) and run is defined as $x_2 - x_1$ (the change in x), the slope of a secant line is:

$$\text{Slope of Secant Line} = \frac{\Delta f}{\Delta x} = \frac{f(x_2) - f(x_1)}{x_2 - x_1}.$$

Now things start to get complicated.

To find the slope at x_1, slide the value of x_2 as close to x_1 as you can get without actually touching it. As you do this both the rise (Δf) and the run (Δx) get smaller and smaller. In other words,

$$\text{Slope at } x_1 = \frac{\Delta f \to 0}{\Delta x \to 0}.$$

If the rise (Δf) approaches zero more quickly than the run, then the slope is zero. If the run (Δx) approaches zero more quickly than the rise, then the slope becomes infinitely large. For most functions, both the rise and the run approach zero in such a way as to produce some non-zero and non-infinite slope. In other words, $\Delta f / \Delta x$ is a real number equal to the slope at x_1.

How mathematicians do this is with **function limits**. Function limits are one of the most difficult concepts for beginning Calculus students to grasp. This is because function limits require a knowledge of logic which isn't taught in High School. Fortunately, you can still understand Calculus and make an A+ without being an expert at function limits.

Mathematicians use the lim symbol for denoting the process of calculating a function limit. For example, the act of sliding the value of x_2 towards x_1 in the secant slope is denoted by:

$$\lim_{x_2 \to x_1} \frac{f(x_2) - f(x_1)}{x_2 - x_1}.$$

When the difference between x_2 and x_1 becomes extremely small, mathematicians stop denoting the difference by Δx and instead denote it by dx. In other words, Δ is a difference and d is a *very* small difference.

Similarly, when the difference between $f(x_2)$ and $f(x_1)$ becomes extremely small, we stop denoting the difference by Δf and instead denote it by df.

This means that

$$\lim_{x_2 \to x_1} \frac{f(x_2) - f(x_1)}{x_2 - x_1} = \lim_{x_2 \to x_1} \frac{\Delta f}{\Delta x} = \frac{df}{dx}.$$

You should recognize from the previous chapter that df/dx is the derivative. In other words,

$$\text{Slope at } x_1 = \text{Derivative at } x_1 = \frac{df}{dx}.$$

Now, let me clarify and explain the notation you'll see in most Calculus textbooks.

First, we typically think of x_2 as being a distance h away from x_1. Mathematically, we write $x_2 = x_1 + h$. This means that $\Delta x = h$ and $f(x_2) = f(x_1 + h)$. As x_2 gets closer and closer to x_1, h gets closer and closer to zero. Therefore,

$$\frac{df}{dx} = \lim_{h \to 0} \frac{f(x_1 + h) - f(x_1)}{h}.$$

Second, while I've talked about finding the value of the slope at x_1, I didn't specify exactly *where* x_1 is on the x-axis. I didn't tell you the value of x_1. When we go through the details of finding the function limit,

$$\frac{df}{dx} = \lim_{h \to 0} \frac{f(x_1 + h) - f(x_1)}{h},$$

we usually don't have to specify where x_1 is at on the x-axis. This is not always true, but the functions you'll deal with in a beginning Calculus class are easy enough that you can find the derivative at x_1 and not actually specify where it is on the x-axis. Since the value of x_1 is not specified, everyone drops the subscript 1 and writes,

$$\frac{df}{dx} = \lim_{h \to 0} \frac{f(x + h) - f(x)}{h}.$$

This formula for a derivative is how you'll see it in almost every introductory textbook on Calculus. It's not a new concept, but only a change in notation. Ideally, I should have initially said something like,

$$\frac{df}{dx_1} = \lim_{h \to 0} \frac{f(x_1 + h) - f(x_1)}{h}$$

to show that the derivative was being calculated at x_1. However, I didn't because I knew I was going to explain it later. And now I have.

It's important to emphasize that I haven't told you *how* to calculate a function limit. It's beyond the scope of trying to learn Calculus in five hours. Keep in mind the idea of x_2 sliding toward x_1, and you'll be fine.

Now that you know what a derivative is, the next task is to learn some basic rules for finding it when given a specific function. The real math is in doing the function limits, but mathematicians have used function limits to find general rules for calculating derivatives so you don't have to do as much work. That's the focus of the next chapter.

Read on . . .

Chapter 6 - Your First Four Derivatives (12 minutes)

In this chapter I'm going to present the four most important rules of derivatives that you must know and memorize. These rules come from logical results and calculations of function limits. Mathematicians have used function limits to come up with these rules so you can find derivatives for a massive number of functions quickly and easily. Knowing and memorizing these formulas is easy. Let's get started.

Rule 1: The Derivative of a Constant

Let's assume that C is a constant number like 2, 17, or 3.141592. The derivative of a constant is zero. In other words,

$$\frac{d}{dx}C = 0.$$

Remember that a derivative is a slope (rise over run). So how much does a constant "rise" when you "run"? It doesn't, and that's why the derivative is zero.

Rule 2: The Derivative of a Constant Times a Function

Let's assume C is a constant number. If $f(x)$ has the derivative df/dx, then the derivative of $C \cdot f(x)$ is

$$\frac{d}{dx}\left[C \cdot f(x)\right] = C \cdot \frac{df}{dx}.$$

And here it is in prime notation:

$$(C \cdot f)'(x) = C \cdot f'(x).$$

Rule 3: The Derivative of the Sum of Two Functions

Let's assume $h(x)$ is the sum of two functions $f(x)$ and $g(x)$. That is, $h(x) = f(x) + g(x)$. If $f(x)$ has the derivative df/dx and $g(x)$ has the derivative dg/dx, then the derivative of $h(x)$ is

$$\begin{aligned} \frac{d}{dx}h(x) &= \frac{d}{dx}\left[f(x) + g(x)\right] \\ &= \frac{df}{dx} + \frac{dg}{dx}. \end{aligned}$$

In other words, just add the derivatives of the individual functions. Sometimes it's helpful to see it in prime notation. Here it is:

$$h'(x) = (f + g)'(x) = f'(x) + g'(x)$$

You can now combine these in obvious and cool ways.

For example, what if you wanted to know the derivative of $f(x) - g(x)$? Think of $-g(x)$ as $C \cdot g(x)$ where $C = -1$. This means you need to find the derivative of $f(x) + C \cdot g(x)$. From Rule 3 you know that

$$\frac{d}{dx}\left[f(x) + C \cdot g(x)\right] = \frac{df}{dx} + \frac{d}{dx}\left[C \cdot g(x)\right].$$

And from Rule 2 you know that

$$\frac{d}{dx}\left[C \cdot g(x)\right] = C \cdot \frac{dg}{dx}.$$

Plugging this back in you have

$$\frac{d}{dx}\left[f(x) + C \cdot g(x)\right] = \frac{df}{dx} + C \cdot \frac{dg}{dx}.$$

Finally, plug in -1 for C to get

$$\frac{d}{dx}\left[f(x) - g(x)\right] = \frac{df}{dx} - \frac{dg}{dx}.$$

With Rules 2 and 3 you discovered the derivative of the subtraction of two functions!

Okay, now for the one of the most important rules in Calculus - **The Power Rule**.

Rule 4: The Power Rule

$$\frac{d}{dx}x^n = nx^{n-1}$$

where n is an integer. (Remember an integer is a number like 1,3 or -100, but not 1.5 or 2.3.)

For example, the Power Rule means the derivative of x is 1, the derivative of x^2 is $2x$, and the derivative of x^3 is $3x^2$. You have to know and memorize the Power Rule!

What if you want to find the derivative of $4x^3$? Think of this as $C \cdot f(x)$ where $C = 4$ and $f(x) = x^3$. Rule 2 says that

$$\frac{d}{dx}\left[C \cdot f(x)\right] = C \cdot \frac{df}{dx}.$$

This means that

$$\frac{d}{dx}\left[4 \cdot x^3\right] = 4 \cdot \frac{d}{dx}x^3,$$

but from the Power Rule

$$\frac{d}{dx}x^3 = 3x^2.$$

This means that

$$\frac{d}{dx}\left[4 \cdot x^3\right] = 4 \cdot 3 \cdot x^2 = 12x^2.$$

The exercise above is the basis for rule 5:

Rule 5: The Derivative of $C\,x^n$

$$\frac{d}{dx}\left[C\,x^n\right] = Cnx^{n-1}$$

where n is an integer and C is a constant. Remember, this comes from rules 2 and 4 so you only need to keep the first four rules in your head!

Next, we'll take a brief aside so you can learn more about the tangent line. We'll get its exact formula and see how it can be used to approximate the value of a function.

Keep reading . . .

Chapter 7 - The Tangent Line (3 minutes)

A Tangent Line is a straight line that touches $f(x)$ at one point and has the same slope as the function at that point.

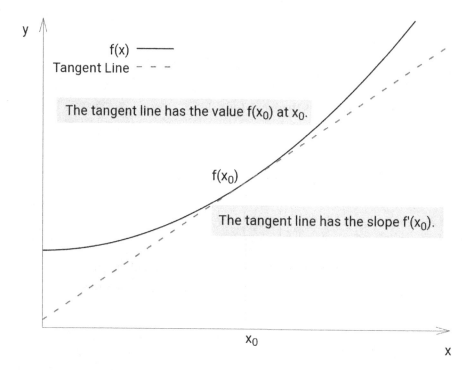

Assume we have a function $f(x)$ and its derivative $f'(x)$. Let's find the formula for the tangent line at any arbitrary point x_0 in terms of $f(x)$ and $f'(x)$.

Since the tangent line is a straight line, it has the formula $y = mx + b$. To accomplish our goal we need to find the value of m and b in terms of $f(x_0)$ and $f'(x_0)$. By definition, the tangent line's slope is equal to the function's slope at x_0. Therefore, $m = f'(x_0)$.

Now let's find b in terms of $f(x_0)$ and $f'(x_0)$. Because we've *defined* the tangent line as touching $f(x)$ at x_0, the tangent line has the value $f(x_0)$ at x_0. Therefore, at x_0 we have $y = f(x_0)$. Now do some algebra to find b:

$$y = mx + b$$
$$f(x_0) = mx_0 + b$$
$$f(x_0) - mx_0 = b.$$

Since $m = f'(x_0)$ we see that $b = f(x_0) - f'(x_0)x_0$.

Plug m and b into $y = mx + b$ to get the formula for the tangent line:

$$y = f'(x_0)x + [f(x_0) - f'(x_0)x_0].$$

Now group terms with $f'(x_0)$ together. This gives you the formula for the tangent line seen in most textbooks:

$$y = f(x_0) + f'(x_0)(x - x_0).$$

This expresses the formula for the tangent line by how far x is from x_0. Once $x - x_0$ is known, it's multiplied by the slope of the line ($f'(x_0)$) to find out how much higher or lower the tangent line is from $f(x_0)$. The distance of how much higher or lower the line is from $f(x_0)$ is given by $f'(x_0)(x - x_0)$. That's because $f'(x_0)$ is how much the straight line rises *per* some amount of run. So we multiply a specific amount of run times the slope to get how much it rises in that amount of run.

Remember that the slope ($f'(x)$) is always the same at every point on a straight line, and it's the amount a line will rise per the amount it runs. $x - x_0$ is an amount of run, and $f'(x_0)(x - x_0)$ is the amount it rises when it runs for a $x - x_0$ amount. Add $f'(x_0)(x - x_0)$ of rise to $f(x_0)$ and you have the value of y at x. See the figure on the next page.

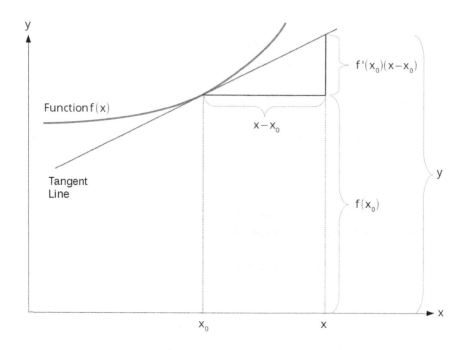

The tangent line formula allows you to *approximate* the value $f(x)$ knowing only its value at x_0 and it's derivative at x_0. The approximation (denoted by $\approx$ instead of =) is:

$$f(x) \approx f(x_0) + f'(x_0)(x - x_0)$$

The further away x is from x_0, the worse $f(x_0) + f'(x_0)(x - x_0)$ is at approximating $f(x)$. However, that's an advanced topic of Calculus best left for another day.

In the next chapter I'll reveal the formula for the derivative of a polynomial. You'll be surprised to find out you already know it.

Read on . . .

Chapter 8 - The Derivative of a Polynomial (16 minutes)

One of the easiest formulas to memorize is the derivative of a polynomial. Recall that the form of a polynomial is

$$f(x) = a_n x^n + a_{n-1} x^{n-1} + \cdots + a_1 x + a_0.$$

Its derivative is:

> ### The Derivative of a Polynomial
>
> If $f(x)$ is the polynomial
>
> $$a_n x^n + a_{n-1} x^{n-1} + \cdots + a_1 x + a_0,$$
>
> then its derivative is
>
> $$\begin{aligned} f'(x) \;=\;\; & n\, a_n x^{n-1} \\ + \;\; & (n-1)\, a_{n-1} x^{n-2} \\ & \vdots \\ + \;\; & a_1. \end{aligned}$$
>
> For every term in the polynomial, multiply the coefficient by the exponent, and then subtracting one from the exponent. In other words, apply the **Power Rule** to every term in the polynomial.

You don't have to memorize this rule because it comes from the first four rules of derivatives you learned in Chapter 6.

Let's do a quick example by finding the derivative of

$$f(x) = 6x^4 + 7x^2 + 8x + 5.$$

Using the rule above we know that

$$
\begin{aligned}
f'(x) &= 4 \cdot 6 \cdot x^{4-1} \\
&+ 2 \cdot 7 \cdot x^{2-1} \\
&+ 1 \cdot 8 \cdot x^{1-1} \\
&+ 0 \cdot 5 \cdot x^{0-1} \\
&= 24x^3 + 14x + 8.
\end{aligned}
$$

In the calculation we viewed 5 as $5x^0$ because $x^0 = 1$. It's derivative is $0 \cdot 5 \cdot x^{-1} = (0 \cdot 5)/x = 0$. In other words, the Power Rule is consistent with the rule that the derivative of a constant is zero.

Exercise: Determine the derivatives of the following polynomials:

- $f(x) = 5x^7 + 16x^3 - 9$ at $x = 4$
- $f(x) = x^2$ at $x = -2.3$
- $f(x) = -2.3x^3 - 5.2$ at $x = -2$
- $f(x) = 16x^3 - 8x^2 + 15x - 22$ at $x = 10$

(Answers: 144110, -4.6, -27.6, and 4655. Go to www.CalculusSolution.com/node/31729 for an interactive calculator to help you out.)

Remember, I showed you how to combine two functions by addition, subtraction, multiplication, division and function composition in Chapter 3. In Chapter 6 you learned the derivative of the addition and subtraction of two functions. In the next three chapters I'll give you the rules for finding the derivative of the multiplication, division, and function composition of two functions. These rules will make finding complex derivatives super easy, so keep reading.

Chapter 9 - The Product Rule (12 minutes)

Chapter 3 was about the five ways you can combine two functions. One of those ways was multiplication. The **Product Rule** is an easy way to find the derivative of the multiplication of two functions.

Let's say you have two functions, $f(x)$ and $g(x)$, and you want to find the derivative of $f(x)g(x)$. Symbolically, you write

$$\frac{d}{dx}fg.$$

There are two ways to find it:

1. Multiply $f(x)$ and $g(x)$ together, and then find the derivative.
2. Find the derivative directly with the Product Rule. (You don't have to multiply $f(x)$ and $g(x)$ together first!)

The Product Rule is the second method, and it allows you to find the derivative without multiplying $f(x)$ and $g(x)$ together like you do in method 1.

The Product Rule

If you already know the derivatives of $f(x)$ and $g(x)$ (df/dx and dg/dx), then the Product Rule states that

$$\frac{d}{dx}fg = g\frac{df}{dx} + f\frac{dg}{dx}.$$

We can also write this in prime notation as

$$(fg)'(x) = g(x) \cdot f'(x) + f(x) \cdot g'(x).$$

Exercise: Find the derivative of the multiplication of the following two functions:

- $f(x) = 4x^2 + 5x - 2$ and $g(x) = -3x - 7$ (Answer: www.CalculusSolution.com/node/31735)
- $f(x) = 5x^6 - 16x^5 - 4x^4 + 72x^3 - 3x^2 - 2x + 18$ and $g(x) = 42x^2 + 32x + 7$ (Answer: www.CalculusSolution.com/node/31736)
- $f(x) = 32x^2 - 23x + 6$ and $g(x) = 4x^2 + 7x + 6$ (Answer: www.CalculusSolution.com/node/31737)

What about the division of two functions? That's the topic of the next chapter . . .

Chapter 10 - The Quotient Rule (13 minutes)

Chapter 3 was about the five ways you can combine two functions. One of those ways was division. The **Quotient Rule** is an easy way to find the derivative of the division of two functions.

Let's say you have two functions, $f(x)$ and $g(x)$, and you want to find the derivative of $f(x)/g(x)$. Symbolically, you write

$$\frac{d}{dx}\left(\frac{f}{g}\right).$$

There are two ways you can find it:

1. Divide $f(x)$ by $g(x)$, and then find the derivative. (Good luck with that!)
2. Find the derivative directly with the Quotient Rule. (You don't have to divide $f(x)$ by $g(x)$ first!)

The Quotient Rule

If you already know the derivatives of $f(x)$ and $g(x)$ (df/dx and dg/dx), then the Quotient Rule states that

$$\frac{d}{dx}\left(\frac{f}{g}\right) = \frac{1}{g^2}\left(g\frac{df}{dx} - f\frac{dg}{dx}\right).$$

We can also write this in prime notation as

$$\left(\frac{f}{g}\right)'(x) = \frac{g(x) \cdot f'(x) - f(x) \cdot g'(x)}{[g(x)]^2}.$$

The Quotient Rule is a rule you have to memorize, so let's do something completely silly to help you memorize it. Let's call the function in the numerator (top function which is $f(x)$) "hi" for high, and call the function in the denominator (bottom function which is $g(x)$) "ho" for low. Instead of d/dx, let's print "D" and say "dee". For example, dg/dx would be "D ho". We can now restate the Quotient Rule as

$$D\left(\frac{\text{hi}}{\text{ho}}\right) = \frac{\text{ho } D\text{hi} - \text{hi } D\text{ho}}{\text{ho ho}}$$

Say "ho dee hi minus hi dee ho over ho ho" out loud a few times, and you'll find you've memorized the Quotient Rule. Just remember that it's "hoDhi" in front of the minus sign, and not "hiDho".

Oh yeah, I think some math teachers use "lo" instead of "ho." That makes sense, of course, but this is how it was originally taught to me, and I can't get it out of my head. Choose lo or ho and stick with it. No matter which one you choose, you'll never forget the Quotient Rule.

Exercise: Find the derivative of the division of the following two functions:

- $f(x) = 4x^2 + 5x - 2$ and $g(x) = -3x - 7$ (Answer: www.CalculusSolution.com/node/31739)
- $f(x) = 5x^6 - 16x^5 - 4x^4 + 72x^3 - 3x^2 - 2x + 18$ and $g(x) = 42x^2 + 32x + 7$ (Answer: www.CalculusSolution.com/node/31741)
- $f(x) = 32x^2 - 23x + 6$ and $g(x) = 4x^2 + 7x + 6$ (Answer: www.CalculusSolution.com/node/31740)

I've shown you how to find the derivative of the addition, subtraction, multiplication, and division of two functions. But what about the derivative of a function composition? Wasn't that the fifth way to combine two functions in Chapter 3? Shouldn't we find *that* derivative since we've found the other four? Absolutely! That's the topic of the next chapter, and it will make some complex derivatives easy to calculate.

Chapter 11 - The Chain Rule (16 minutes)

Recall, in function composition you obtain $(f \circ g)(x) = f(g(x))$ by placing g into every value of x in $f(x)$ to obtain $f(g)$. Then you put the formula for $g(x)$ into every value of g in $f(g)$.

Now, once you have the formula for $(f \circ g)(x)$, use the rules you already know to find its derivative. In prime notation we write the derivative of $(f \circ g)(x)$ as $(f \circ g)'(x)$.

For example, if $f(x) = x^3 + 3$ and $g(x) = x + 2$, then

$$
\begin{aligned}
(f \circ g)(x) &= f(g(x)), \\
&= (x+2)^3 + 3, \\
&= (x+2)(x+2)(x+2) + 3, \\
&= (x^2 + 4x + 4)(x+2) + 3,
\end{aligned}
$$
and
$$
= x^3 + 6x^2 + 12x + 11.
$$

Because $(f \circ g)(x)$ is a polynomial we can determine its derivative. It is

$$(f \circ g)'(x) = 3x^2 + 12x + 12.$$

Finding $(f \circ g)'(x)$ was difficult because you had to find the formula for $(f \circ g)(x)$ first. But what if you could find $(f \circ g)'(x)$ without having to find $(f \circ g)(x)$ first? Wouldn't that be easier? This is where the Chain Rule comes in handy.

Recall that there are two notations for denoting a derivative: $f'(x)$ and df/dx. It's helpful to state the Chain Rule using both notations:

The Chain Rule (in df/dx notation)

$$\frac{d}{dx}[f \circ g] = \frac{df}{dg} \cdot \frac{dg}{dx}$$

This notation is useful because it provides an easy way to keep the rule in your head. Let's call $e(x) = f(g(x))$. Since $e(x) = (f \circ g)(x)$ the Chain Rule is equivalent to finding de/dx. Remember that anything divided by itself is 1. So $1 = dg/dg$. Therefore,

$$\frac{de}{dx} = \frac{de}{dx} \cdot 1 = \frac{de}{dx} \cdot \frac{dg}{dg} = \frac{de}{dg} \cdot \frac{dg}{dx}.$$

But $de/dg = df/dg$ because $e = f(g)$. Therefore,

$$\frac{de}{dx} = \frac{df}{dg} \cdot \frac{dg}{dx}.$$

What I just did is <u>not</u> a logical proof. It's a complex but useful way to keep the rule in your head.

In the $f'(x)$ notation the Chain Rule is:

The Chain Rule (in $f'(x)$ notation)

$$(f \circ g)'(x) = f'(g(x))\, g'(x)$$

To get the hang of the Chain Rule, it helps to have a step-by-step procedure. Here it is along with the example of finding $(f \circ g)'(x)$ for $f(x) = x^3 + 3$ and $g(x) = x + 2$:

Step	Example
Determine df/dx and dg/dx.	$\dfrac{df}{dx} = 3x^2$ and $\dfrac{dg}{dx} = 1$
Place g in for every value of x in df/dx. Call this df/dg.	$\dfrac{df}{dg} = 3g^2$
Place the function $g(x)$ into every value of g in df/dg. Continue to call this df/dg.	$\dfrac{df}{dg} = 3(x+2)^2$
Multiply dg/dx times df/dg. This is $\frac{d}{dx}[f \circ g]$.	$\dfrac{df}{dg} \cdot \dfrac{dg}{dx} = \left[3(x+2)^2\right] \cdot 1$
If needed, do some algebra to simplify or expand the answer.	$\dfrac{df}{dg} \cdot \dfrac{dg}{dx} = 3x^2 + 12x + 12$

It worked! Using the Chain Rule gave us the same answer.

In summary, there are two ways to find the derivative of $(f \circ g)(x)$:

- Find $(f \circ g)(x)$ and determine its derivative.
- Apply the Chain Rule knowing the derivatives of $f(x)$ and $g(x)$.

One of the most important places the Chain Rule is used is in the solution of problems of the form $[f(x)]^n$. Think of this as a function composition and find the derivative using the Chain Rule.

Let's say that $u(x) = x^n$. Then

$$[f(x)]^n = u(f(x)) = (u \circ f)(x),$$

and we know from the Chain Rule that

$$\frac{d}{dx}\left[[f(x)]^n\right] = n\,[f(x)]^{n-1} \cdot \frac{df}{dx}.$$

Try finding the derivative of $(x^2 - 1)^{50}$ by directly expanding it and then finding its derivative. Expanding it will take you forever, and then you'll still have to calculate the derivative! With the Chain Rule it only takes a second. Problems like this make you appreciate the Chain Rule.

Exercises:

- Find the derivative of $(x^2 - 1)^{50}$. (Answer www.CalculusSolution.com/node/31743.)
- Find $(f \circ g)'(x)$ where $f(x) = 3x^2 + 5x - 2$ and $g(x) = 4x + 3$. (Answer www.CalculusSolution.com/node/31744.)
- Find $(g \circ f)'(x)$ where $f(x) = 3x^2 + 5x - 2$ and $g(x) = 4x + 3$. Notice we did $(f \circ g)'(x)$ in the previous problem. (Answer www.CalculusSolution.com/node/31745.)

In two of the exercises you're asked to find the two function compositions $(f \circ g)'(x)$ and $(g \circ f)'(x)$ for $f(x) = 3x^2 + 5x - 2$ and $g(x) = 4x + 3$. Notice that $(f \circ g)'(x) \neq (g \circ f)'(x)$. This comes from the general rule that the function compositions $(f \circ g)(x)$ and $(g \circ f)(x)$ are not guaranteed to be equal. So their derivatives aren't guaranteed to be equal either.

Okay, now you know what a derivative is and some of the most important rules for finding it. The next step is to connect functions and their derivatives to the real world.

Onward . . .

Chapter 12 - Attaching Real World Meaning to Variables and Functions (7 minutes)

If someone came up to you and said they had "four," what would your reaction be? For most people the response would be, "Four what?" The what is called a **unit** or **dimension**, and it lets you know what a number means.

A person could be referring to four inches, four feet, four dollars, or four apples. If someone said they had four oranges, then the unit would be oranges.

The most important system of units is the **International System of Units** which is typically abbreviated SI. This system is defined by seven fundamental units. Here are four of them:

Physical Quantity	Name	Abbreviation
Mass	Kilograms	kg
Length	Meters	m
Time	Seconds	s
Temperature	Kelvins	K

More importantly, all physical quantities are made up of these fundamental units. For example:

Physical Quantity	Name	Abbreviation
Speed	Meters per Second	m/s
Acceleration	Meters per Second-squared	m/s^2
Force	Newtons	$kg \cdot m/s^2$
Energy	Joules	$kg \cdot m^2/s^2$

This means that the units of energy are kilograms times mass-squared divided by seconds-squared. That's a lot to say, so we call the units of energy Joules after James Prescott Joule who studied the nature of heat energy and its relationship to mechanical work.

Outside of communicating what we're talking about, units play a special role in how to describe the real world with mathematics. Ask yourself this simple question, "Is an apple the same as an orange?" No, it's not.

Similarly, for a mathematical equation to describe the real world, the units on the left side of an equal sign must be the same as the units on the right side of the equal sign.

The process of determining if the units on the left side of an equal sign are equal to the units on the right side of an equal sign is called **dimensional analysis**.

For example, the force of gravity between two objects is given by the equation

$$F = G\frac{m_1 m_2}{r^2}$$

where r is the distance between the two masses m_1 and m_2. G is the gravitational constant which has a value of $6.67 \times 10^{-11} m^3/kg\, s^2$. Finally, F is the force in Newtons.

To see if this equation is physically valid, do a dimensional analysis. In a dimensional analysis you don't worry about putting in numbers. Place each quantity's unit in the equation like this:

$$kg\, m/s^2 = \left\{ \frac{m^3}{kg \cdot s^2} \right\} \frac{kg \cdot kg}{m^2}$$

Now cancel terms according to the rules of algebra. (Notice that the kg on the bottom will cancel with one of the kg's in the top. Also, the two m's (m^2) in the bottom will cancel with two on the top.) Doing this gives:

$$\frac{kg \cdot m}{s^2} = \left\{ \frac{m^3}{kg \cdot s^2} \right\} \frac{kg \cdot kg}{m^2}$$

$$\frac{kg \cdot m}{s^2} = \frac{kg \cdot m}{s^2}.$$

Both sides of the equal sign have the same unit of Newtons ($kg \cdot m/s^2$) so it's a valid equation for describing the real world.

While dimensional analysis won't tell you if an equation is correct or not, it's always the first step to see if an equation can describe the real world. <u>If the units on the left-hand side don't equal the units on the right-hand side, it can't be used to model the real world.</u>

When you describe the real world, a variable (like x) will have a unit, and a function (like $f(x)$) will also have unit. The units for x and $f(x)$ could be the same or they could be different from each other.

For example, scientists know the average height of a person as a function of their age. We can have the function $h(a)$ represent the average height of a person when they are at an age of a. So h has a unit of feet, and the variable a has a unit of years (the number of years alive). This function could look something like

$$h(a) = \begin{cases} \left(0.22\frac{\text{feet}}{\text{years}}\right) a + 1.67\text{feet}, & 0 \leq a \leq 18\text{years} \\ 5.67\text{feet}, & a > 18\text{years} \end{cases}$$

The important thing to notice is that the units have been placed into the equation just like any number or variable would be. For example, if the number 3.5 was in an equation and you wanted to put in its unit, you would **multiply** the unit times 3.5. So if the unit was inches, 3.5 inches means 3.5 *times* inches where inches is treated like a variable. And once the unit is in the equation (by multiplying it times the number it is referring to), it is treated as a variable with the same algebraic rules applied to it as are applied to any other number or variable in the equation.

Let's say we want to see how tall someone will be at an age of 4 years. Let's go through the steps:

$$
\begin{aligned}
h(4\text{years}) \;&=\; \left(0.22\frac{\text{feet}}{\text{years}}\right)4\text{years} + 1.67\text{feet} \\[2mm]
&=\; 0.22 \cdot 4 \cdot \frac{\text{feet}}{\text{years}} \cdot \text{years} + 1.67\text{feet} \\[2mm]
&=\; 0.88\text{feet} + 1.67\text{feet} \\[2mm]
&=\; 2.55\text{feet}.
\end{aligned}
$$

When all the calculations on the right are done, h must be a number with units of feet. This emphasizes the point made previously that the units on the left side of the equal sign must equal the units on the right side of the equal sign.

Remember, when you add (or subtract) elements in a function they must all have the same unit. For example, if $h(x) = f(x) + g(x)$, then h, f, and g must all have the same unit.

Now you know about units and how they're used to describe the real world. In the next chapter I'll tell you what the real world meaning of a derivative is.

Keep reading . . .

Chapter 13 - Attaching Real World Meaning to Derivatives (13 minutes)

In the previous chapter you learned how variables and functions have a unit attached to them.

Now, pretend you drive from Chicago to New York city, and as you drive you record the distance you travel and the number of hours since you left.

This is a function, so let's denote it by $d(t)$. The variable d is the distance measured in miles (miles is the unit of d), and t is the number of hours since you left (hours is the unit of t).

By now you know that slope is the amount a straight line "rises" in some amount of "run." The slope of a secant line is:

$$\text{Secant Slope} = \frac{\Delta f}{\Delta x}.$$

In other words, $\Delta f/\Delta x$ is the amount $f(x)$ changes per some amount of change in x. *We refer to this as a **rate of change**, and it is the real world meaning of a slope.*

This is extremely important and cannot be emphasized enough. Slope is a rate of change - the amount $f(x)$ changes during some amount of change in x.

Let me explain this with the example of traveling from Chicago to New York. To get an intuitive feel for this you have to know what unit the slope has. **The unit of the slope is the unit of $f(x)$ divided by the unit of x.**

In the current example, the function is $d(t)$ where d is the distance measured in miles, and t is the number of hours since you left Chicago. So the slope, $\Delta d/\Delta t$, has a unit of <u>miles per hour</u>. This is speed! Speed is the change in your distance divided by the amount of time you traveled. Speed is the slope $\Delta d/\Delta t$!

But you also know that a derivative is a slope - the slope of a tangent line at a specific point on a function. Therefore, a derivative is also a rate of change. It's how much $f(x)$ is changing at the point x.

So what's the difference between the slope of a derivative (tangent line) and the slope of a secant line? If both are rates of change, what do they mean? Is there a difference?

Yes, there is a difference. The slope of a secant line is an **average rate of change** between two points, and the derivative is an **instantaneous rate of change** at a single point.

Rate of Change of Functions

The **average rate of change** of a function $f(x)$ between two points, x_1 and x_2, is

$$\text{Average Rate of Change} = \frac{f(x_2) - f(x_1)}{x_2 - x_1}$$

where $x_1 < x_2$. The average rate of change is the slope of the secant line between x_1 and x_2.

The function's **instantaneous rate of change** at a specific point, x, is its derivative $f'(x)$.

$$\text{Instantaneous Rate of Change} = f'(x).$$

The instantaneous rate of change is the slope of the tangent line at x.

Let me demonstrate the difference between an average rate of change and an instantaneous rate of change using our current example of driving from Chicago to New York.

What we want to know is what the real world difference between $\Delta d/\Delta t$ and $d'(t)$ is. Let's say you drove straight through without stopping, and it took you 12.5 hours to drive the 800 miles between the two cities. So,

$$\frac{\Delta d}{\Delta t} = \frac{800\text{miles}}{12.5\text{hours}} = 64\text{miles per hour.}$$

This average rate of change is your **average speed** driving from Chicago to New York.

But your speed is NOT constant. You speed up to pass other cars, slow down for construction, and you make rest stops.

At any time you can look down at your speedometer to see how fast you're going. The speed you see when you look at your speedometer is $d'(t)$.

The **instantaneous rate of change**, $d'(t)$, is the **instantaneous speed** you see on your speedometer!

The rest of this chapter is meant to drive home the concept that slope is a rate of change and to emphasize there are two kinds of slopes. The slope of a secant line is an **average rate of change**, and the slope of a tangent line is an **instantaneous rate of change**.

First, take a look at the distance-time function pictured on the next page. You'll see times when the car is speeding up, slowing down, and stopped.

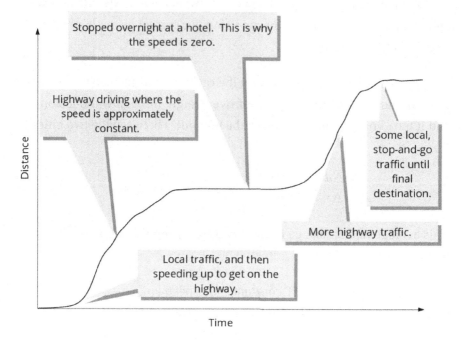

Next, let's do a simple example. Suppose,

$$d(t) = \left(\frac{t - 7.38\text{hours}}{\text{hours}}\right)^3 \cdot \text{miles} + 401.95\text{miles}.$$

Using derivative rules one and three in Chapter 6 and the Chain Rule, you know that

$$d'(t) = 3(t - 7.38\text{hours})^2 \cdot \frac{\text{miles}}{\text{hours}^3}.$$

You can now answer questions like:

1. What's the average speed between hours 3 and 10?
2. What's the instantaneous speed at hour 4?

Let's answer the first question now. Here are the steps:

$$\text{Average Speed} = \frac{\Delta d}{\Delta t}$$
$$= \frac{d(10\text{hours}) - d(3\text{hours})}{10\text{hours} - 3\text{hours}}$$
$$= \frac{419.93\text{miles} - 317.92\text{miles}}{10\text{hours} - 3\text{hours}}$$
$$= 14.57\text{miles per hour}$$

Answering the second question is easy. Just plug 4hours into $d'(t)$ like so:

$$d'(4\text{hours}) = 3(4\text{hours} - 7.38\text{hours})^2 \cdot \frac{\text{miles}}{\text{hours}^3}$$
$$= 34.27\text{miles per hour}$$

Exercise: Assume you have a car whose distance-time function is $d(t) = t^3 - 15t^2 + 75t$. Answer the following:

- What is its average speed between an hour and a half and a half hour after it starts its trip? (Answer: www.CalculusSolution.com/node/31750.)
- What is its speed three quarters of an hour after it starts its trip? (Answer: www.CalculusSolution.com/node/31749.)

Now that you know $d'(t)$ is a car's speed, you may be wondering, "What's the car's acceleration?" Great question. Turn the page for the answer.

Chapter 14 - Second Derivatives (10 minutes)

Given any $f(x)$, you know how to find the derivative $f'(x)$. Since $f'(x)$ is another function, can't you find *its* derivative? Yes!

When you find a derivative's derivative its called the **second derivative**, and it's denoted by either $f''(x)$ or d^2f/dx^2.

To find a function's second derivative, apply any of the same rules for finding a derivative to the function $f'(x)$. Here's a quick example:

$$
\begin{aligned}
f(x) &= 3x^2 + 2x + 5 \\
f'(x) &= 6x + 2 \\
f''(x) &= 6.
\end{aligned}
$$

The point is that I treated $f'(x)$ like any other function and applied the rules to it. There's nothing more to finding the second derivative than that.

Exercise: Find the second derivative of $f(x) = -5x^3 + 17x^2 - 5x + 3$. (Answer: www.CalculusSolution.com/node/31752.)

What's important to understand about the second derivative is its meaning. Because it's the derivative of the first derivative, $f'(x)$, the second derivative is a measure of how much the first derivative will rise as it runs from left to right on the x-axis. In other words, it's the rate of change of the first derivative.

Because the first derivative is the slope at a specific point on the function, the second derivative will measure how fast the slope is increasing or decreasing at that point. **If the slope of a function is increasing, then $f''(x) > 0$. If the slope of a function is decreasing, then $f''(x) < 0$.**

The second derivative tells you how the slope is changing. To understand this fully, consider the points x_1 and x_2 on the x-axis, and assume that $x_1 < x_2$. As we go from x_1 to x_2, how will the slope of the function change? In other words, how does $f'(x_1)$ compare to $f'(x_2)$? There are four cases to consider:

1. The current slope is positive ($f'(x_1) > 0$), and the second derivative is positive ($f''(x_1) > 0$).
2. The current slope is positive ($f'(x_1) > 0$), and the second derivative is negative ($f''(x_1) < 0$).
3. The current slope is negative ($f'(x_1) < 0$), and the second derivative is positive ($f''(x_1) > 0$).
4. The current slope is negative ($f'(x_1) < 0$), and the second derivative is negative ($f''(x_1) < 0$).

The pictures on the next four pages deal with each of these cases:

1) The current slope is positive, and the second derivative is positive.

The second derivative is how the first derivative changes. As we go from left to right on the graph, the slope will gain a positive amount. It becomes steeper.

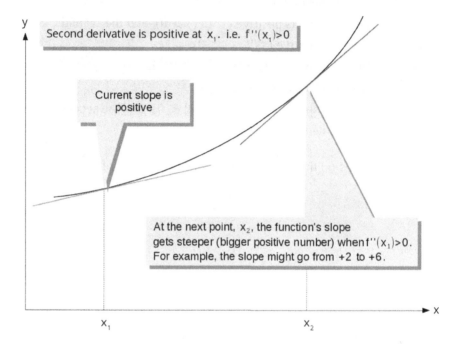

Second derivative is positive at x_1. i.e. $f''(x_1)>0$

Current slope is positive

At the next point, x_2, the function's slope gets steeper (bigger positive number) when $f''(x_1)>0$. For example, the slope might go from +2 to +6.

x_1

x_2

2) The current slope is positive, and the second derivative is negative.

The second derivative is how the first derivative changes. As we go from left to right on the graph, the slope will lose a positive amount. It becomes less steep.

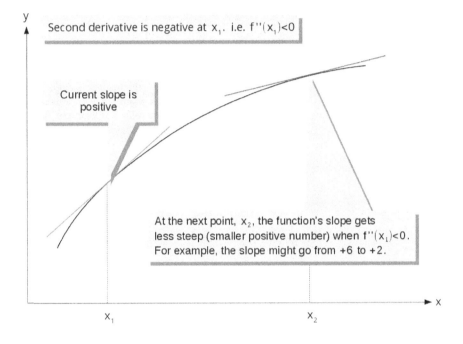

3) The current slope is negative, and the second derivative is positive.

The second derivative is how the first derivative changes. As we go from left to right on the graph, the slope will gain a positive amount. It becomes less negatively steep.

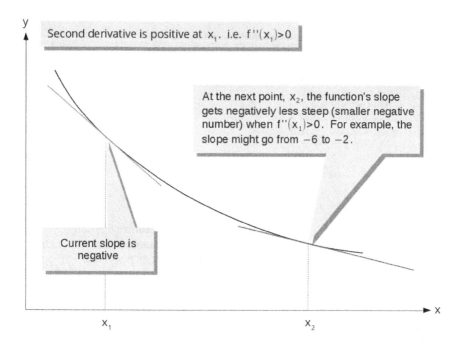

Second derivative is positive at x_1. i.e. $f''(x_1) > 0$

At the next point, x_2, the function's slope gets negatively less steep (smaller negative number) when $f''(x_1) > 0$. For example, the slope might go from -6 to -2.

Current slope is negative

x_1

x_2

4) The current slope is negative, and the second derivative is negative.

The second derivative is how the first derivative changes. As we go from left to right on the graph, the slope will lose a positive amount. It becomes more negatively steep.

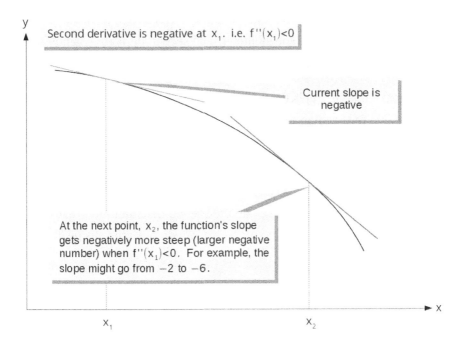

Second derivative is negative at x_1. i.e. $f''(x_1) < 0$

Current slope is negative

At the next point, x_2, the function's slope gets negatively more steep (larger negative number) when $f''(x_1) < 0$. For example, the slope might go from -2 to -6.

Because the **second derivative** is the rate of change of the first derivative, it explains two important concepts:

- how fast the function is increasing or decreasing, and
- how the function is curved.

(How a function is curved is called concavity. Don't worry. I explain it in Chapter 22.)

When I say that the second derivative explains how fast something is increasing or decreasing, it's best to think about the car example in the previous chapter.

Recall that a derivative is a rate of change. It tells you how much $f(x)$ changes per change in x at a specific point. It's an instantaneous rate of change as opposed to an average rate of change.

When you find the second derivative you're finding the derivative of a derivative. In other words, you're finding how fast the derivative changes per change in x.

In the car example, you know that the derivative of distance, $d'(t)$, is the speed you see on the speedometer. The second derivative is how fast your speed is changing. That's acceleration!

That's right, $d''(t)$ is the acceleration of your car. When $d''(t)$ is positive you're speeding up, and when it's negative you're slowing down.

To summarize:

- $d(t)$ is the distance a car has traveled at time t,
- $d'(t)$ is the speed you see on the speedometer at time t, and
- $d''(t)$ is the acceleration of the car as you push the gas peddle or apply the brake.

This is the most common example of using first and second derivatives to describe real-world events. Keep this in your head!

Congratulations! You know a lot about derivatives. You should feel proud of how much you've learned and accomplished.

This ends Part 2, and we're on to Part 3 where I show you how to use first and second derivatives to describe the way a function increases and decreases.

Oh yeah, this is a good time to take a break. You deserve it. But don't wait too long to come back. Learning is best done with speed and intensity.

Part 3 - The Geometry of Functions (67 minutes)

In this part I'll discuss what I call the Geometry of Functions. Just as we can describe a person's face as having two eyes, a nose, two ears, a chin, forehead, etc., we can also name and describe the visual parts of a function.

There's a lot of definitions and concepts in this part. I find it helpful to have an outline of how all the words are related. Hopefully, the outline below will help you keep everything straight.

- Chapter 15 - The Mean-Value Theorem (10 minutes)
- **Increasing and Decreasing Functions**
    - Chapter 16 - Increasing and Decreasing Functions (2 minutes)
    - Chapter 17 - Using Derivatives To Find Where A Function Increases and Decreases (18 minutes)
    - Chapter 18 - Critical Points (4 minutes)
- **Maxima and Minima**
    - Chapter 19 - Maxima and Minima (1 minute)
    - Chapter 20 - The Relationship Between Maxima, Minima, and Critical Points (7 minutes)
    - Chapter 21 - Using Derivatives To Find Maxima and Minima (7 minutes)
- **Concavity**
    - Chapter 22 - Concavity (8 minutes)
    - Chapter 23 - Using Second Derivatives To Determine Concavity (3 minutes)
    - Chapter 24 - Inflection Points (10 minutes)

Let's begin . . .

Chapter 15 - The Mean-Value Theorem (7 minutes)

The beauty of the **Mean-Value Theorem** is that you can look at a picture and realize it's true. So here it is:

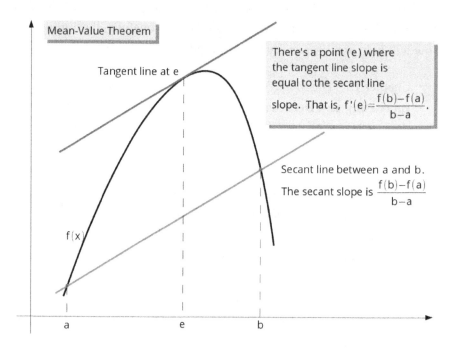

Mean-Value Theorem

Tangent line at e

There's a point (e) where the tangent line slope is equal to the secant line slope. That is, $f'(e) = \dfrac{f(b)-f(a)}{b-a}$.

Secant line between a and b. The secant slope is $\dfrac{f(b)-f(a)}{b-a}$

$f(x)$

Now let me state it in words:

The Mean-Value Theorem

If you make a secant line on $f(x)$ between the points a and b, then there is a point between a and b (let's call it e) where $f'(e)$ is the same slope as the secant line. In other words,

$$f'(e) = \frac{f(b) - f(a)}{b - a}.$$

The steps for doing this are as follows:

- Calculate the slope of the secant line with the formula $[f(b) - f(a)]/[b - a]$
- Find the derivative of $f(x)$
- Set $f'(x) = [f(b) - f(a)]/[b - a]$
- Use High School algebra to find the value of x. This is the point e. (Note there could be more than one point where the slope equals the secant line slope.)

Exercise: Find the point e where the derivative equals the secant line slope for $f(x) = x^2 - 5$ between $a = -101$ and $b = 32$. (Answer:-34.50.)

You can play with this more at www.CalculusSolution.com/lc5h/ mean-value-theorem where there's an interactive Mean-Value Calculator.

Next, I'm going to talk about increasing and decreasing functions. They're easy, so keep reading.

Chapter 16 - Increasing and Decreasing Functions (2 minutes)

This is one of the easiest things to understand in Calculus because we only have to look at three pictures. **An increasing function is one where, as we go from left to right on the graph, the function will be getting higher.** The figure below illustrates this.

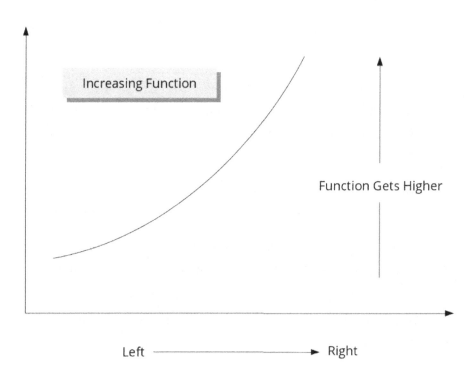

A decreasing function is one where, as we go from left to right on the graph, the function will be getting lower. Again, the figure below illustrates this.

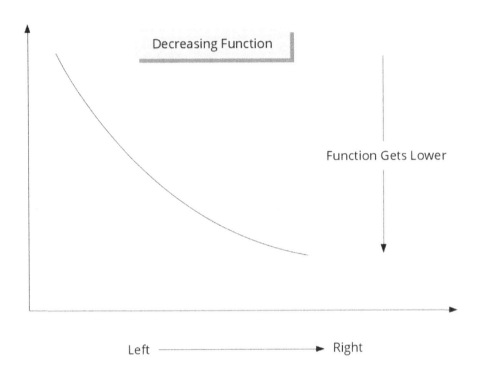

Typically, when we talk about a function increasing or decreasing, we don't mean the function over the whole *domain*. The function can increase or decrease over different parts of the domain. The picture on the next page shows a function increasing over an interval on the x-axis, then decreasing over another, and then finally increasing over a third interval.

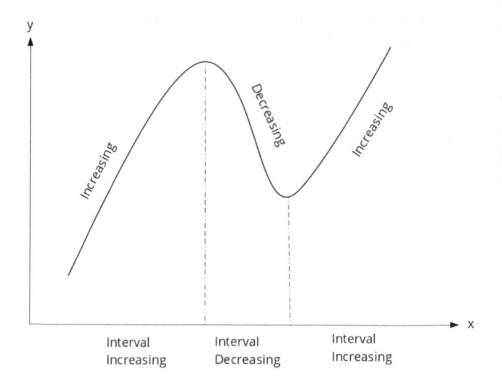

Interval
Increasing

Interval
Decreasing

Interval
Increasing

Like I said, this chapter was easy. Keep going to see how derivatives are used to find when a function is increasing or decreasing.

Chapter 17 - Using Derivatives to Find Where a Function Increases and Decreases (15 minutes)

In this chapter I'm going to show how derivatives are related to whether a function is increasing or not. But before we get to functions in general, let's focus on straight lines. Recall that a straight line's slope is

$$\text{Straight Line Slope} = \frac{f(b) - f(a)}{b - a}$$

where a and b are *any* two points on the x-axis, and $a < b$.

For an increasing straight line, $f(b)$ is higher than $f(a)$. This means that both $f(b) - f(a)$ and $b - a$ are positive. Therefore, the straight line's slope will be *positive*.

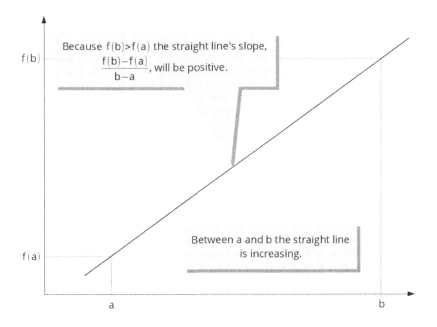

Similarly, for a decreasing straight line, $f(b)$ is lower than $f(a)$. In this case, $f(b) - f(a)$ will be negative while $b - a$ is positive. This means the decreasing straight line's slope will be *negative*.

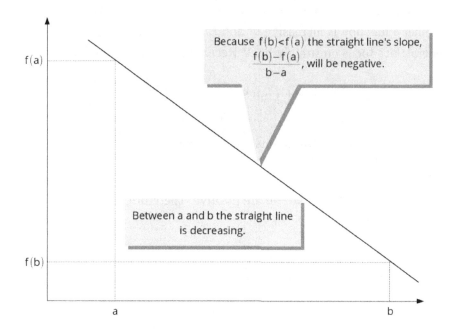

Because $f(b)<f(a)$ the straight line's slope, $\dfrac{f(b)-f(a)}{b-a}$, will be negative.

Between a and b the straight line is decreasing.

Exercise: Determine whether the following straight lines are increasing or decreasing from their slope:

- $f(x) = 5x - 3$ (Answer: The slope is +5, so the function is increasing.)
- $f(x) = -8x + 73$ (Answer: The slope is negative (-8), so the function is decreasing.)

The problem with functions that are not straight lines (for example polynomials) is that you can't look at the slope of the secant line between a and b to see whether the function is increasing or decreasing between a and b.

For example, take a look at the picture below. It shows that the slope of the secant line between a and b is positive (increasing) while at the same time the function is always increasing.

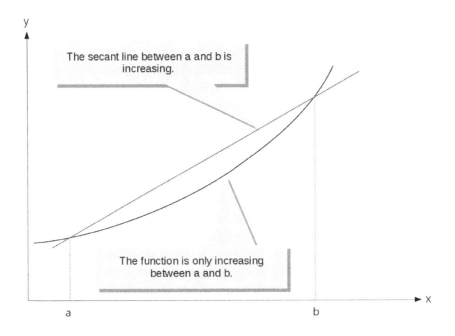

However, take a look at a different function pictured on the next page. It clearly shows that the secant line between a and b is increasing, but the function has places where it's both increasing and decreasing between a and b. You can't look at the slope of the secant line between a and b to see whether the function is increasing or decreasing between those two points.

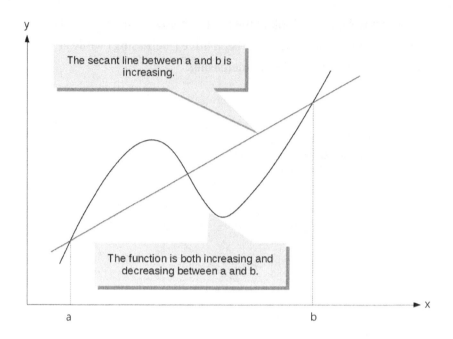

So how can you know if a function is increasing or decreasing without looking at a picture? **For an increasing function all of the derivatives between** a **and** b **will be positive. For a decreasing function all the derivatives between** a **and** b **will be negative.** Memorize this.

Let's go back to our previous two pictures to demonstrate this. In the picture on the next page the function is increasing. The important thing to note is that if we pick *any arbitrary point* between a and b, we'll find that $f'(x)$ is always positive.

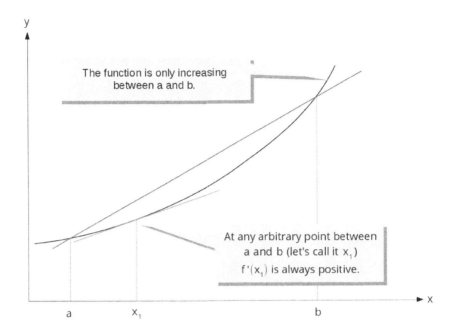

The function is only increasing between a and b.

At any arbitrary point between a and b (let's call it x_1) $f'(x_1)$ is always positive.

However, if we find even *one* point where $f'(x)$ is negative, then we can't say the function is *always* increasing. There will be places between a and b where the function decreases. Take a look at the picture on the next page. Between a and b the function is both increasing and decreasing. If we only looked at the slope of the secant line to determine if the function was increasing or decreasing, we would be deceived. The function is doing both. We can immediately show that it is also decreasing by find a point between a and b where the derivative is negative.

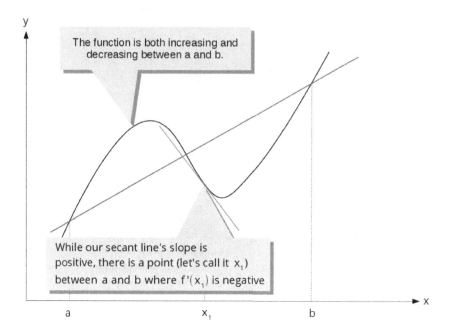

The function is both increasing and decreasing between a and b.

While our secant line's slope is positive, there is a point (let's call it x_1) between a and b where $f'(x_1)$ is negative

So let's review:

Using Derivatives to Find If $f(x)$ Is Increasing or Decreasing Between Two Points, a and b

- If $f'(x) > 0$ for <u>every</u> point between a and b, then $f(x)$ is increasing between a and b.
- If $f'(x) < 0$ for <u>every</u> point between a and b, then $f(x)$ is decreasing between a and b.

Exercise: Show that $f(x) = x^2$ is <u>not</u> a decreasing function between $a = -10$ and $b = 2$ by evaluating $f'(1)$. (Answer at www.CalculusSolution.com/node/31756.)

Next up: critical points. You'll use them to find the tops of hills and the bottoms of valleys.

Onward . . .

Chapter 18 - Critical Points (6 minutes)

A **critical point is where a function's derivative is zero.** In other words, those points on the x-axis where $f'(x) = 0$ are critical points. At a critical point the function is neither increasing nor decreasing. Memorize this paragraph.

Let's do a quick example. Look at the function $f(x) = x^4 - 10x^3$. In the graph below it looks like there are two points where the derivative is zero: $x = 0$ and somewhere around $x = 7$.

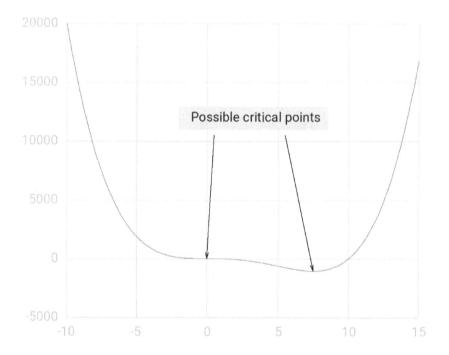

Let's run through the process of finding where the derivative is zero.

First, find the derivative. It's $f'(x) = 4x^3 - 30x^2$.

Next, set the derivative equal to zero and find the values of x that make it zero. Here's the algebra to do that:

$$f'(x) \quad = \quad 4x^3 - 30x^2 = 0$$
$$= \quad x^2 \left(4x - 30\right) = 0.$$

Now, $f'(x)$ will be zero when $x^2 = 0$ and when $4x - 30 = 0$. This means that $f'(x) = 0$ has two critical points. One is at $x = 0$, and the other is at $x = 30/4 = 7.5$.

Exercise: Determine the critical points of $f(x) = (x + 2)^2$. (Answer: It has only one critical point at x=-2. For the details go to www.CalculusSolution.com/node/31761.)

Critical points are easy. There's not much to them, but they're important because they help you identify the maxima and minima of a function. "What are those?" you ask. Keep reading.

Chapter 19 - Maxima and Minima (1 minute)

Think of a **maximum** as the top of a hill and a **minimum** as the bottom of a valley. See the picture below.

A function can have none, one, or more than one maximum or minimum. In the next chapter I'll show you how to use derivatives to find the maxima (plural of maximum) and minima (plural of minimum) of a function.

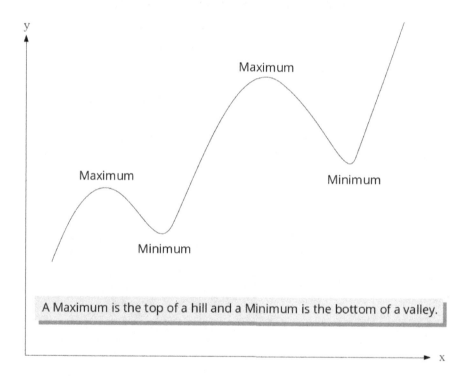

A Maximum is the top of a hill and a Minimum is the bottom of a valley.

This was probably the easiest chapter in the book. In the next chapter I'll show you how to use critical points to find the maxima and minima of a function without looking at it.

Chapter 20 - The Relationship Between Maxima, Minima, and Critical Points (5 minutes)

With the picture below you should see that where there is a maximum, there is also a critical point. This comes from the fact that as we go from the part of the function that is increasing (positive slope) to the part that is decreasing (negative slope), there is some point in between where the slope is zero (a critical point).

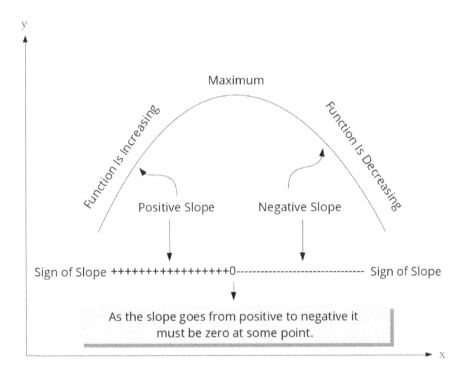

Similarly, where there is a minimum, there is also a critical point. This comes from the fact that as we go from the part of the function that is decreasing (negative slope) to the part that is increasing (positive slope), there is some point in between where the slope is zero (a critical point).

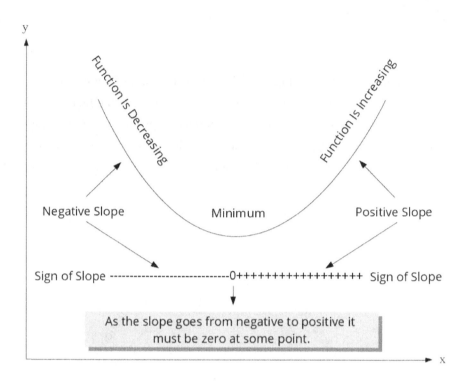

This leads us to an important understanding of maxima, minima, and critical points. **Where there is a maximum or minimum, there is also a critical point!**

However, you need to be careful. Having a critical point does NOT mean you're guaranteed to have a maximum or minimum. The most common example of this is the function $f(x) = x^3$. It's derivative is $f'(x) = 3x^2$, and it has a critical point at $x = 0$. However, as the graph of $f(x) = x^3$ on the next page shows, at $x = 0$ there isn't a minimum or a maximum.

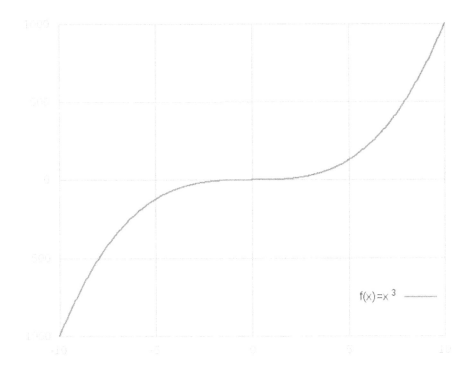

So what good does this relationship between maxima, minima, and critical points do for you? It allows you to find maxima and minima quickly.

The first step to finding a maximum or minimum is to find all the critical points. **We know that if there are any maxima or minima on the function, they'll be <u>at</u> the critical points.**

But once we've found all the critical points, we need to look at each one and do some additional testing to determine if it's a maximum, minimum, or neither as is the case for $f(x) = x^3$.

In the next chapter I'll show you how to determine if a critical point is a maximum or minimum or neither.

Chapter 21 - Using Derivatives to Find Maxima and Minima (12 minutes)

The first step in finding the maxima and minima of a function is to find all the critical points. We know if there are maxima or minima on the function, they will be at the critical points.

Next, look at each critical point to determine whether there is a maximum or minimum there.

In the previous chapter I showed that when you have a maximum the slope is positive right before the critical point and negative right after the critical point. So can't we look at the slope to the left and to the right of each critical point to find a maximum? Yes we can. Doing this is called the **First Derivative Test**.

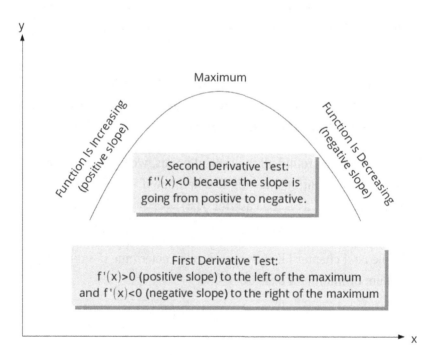

Also, for a maximum this means that as we go from left to right on the graph the first derivative goes from being positive to being negative. So what do we call the change in the first derivative as we go from left to right? The **second derivative**! This means that the second derivative at the critical point is negative! We call this the **Second Derivative Test**.

To summarize, here are the two ways you can determine if a critical point is a maximum:

Determining If a Critical Point Is a Maximum

If e is a critical point, then we can determine if e is a maximum in one of two ways:

- **First Derivative Test:** If $f'(x) > 0$ immediately to the left of e and $f'(x) < 0$ immediately to the right of e, then there is a maximum at e.
- **Second Derivative Test:** If $f''(e) < 0$, then there is a maximum at e. This is because the first derivative is going from positive to negative so its change is negative.

Similarly, when you have a minimum the slope is negative right before the critical point and positive right after the critical point. So can't we look at the slope to the left and to the right of each critical point to find a minimum? Yes, and again this is called the **First Derivative Test**.

Also, for a minimum this means that as we go from left to right on the graph the first derivative goes from being negative to being positive. Again, the change in the first derivative as we go from left to right is the **second derivative**. This means that the second derivative at the critical point is positive! We call this the **Second Derivative Test**.

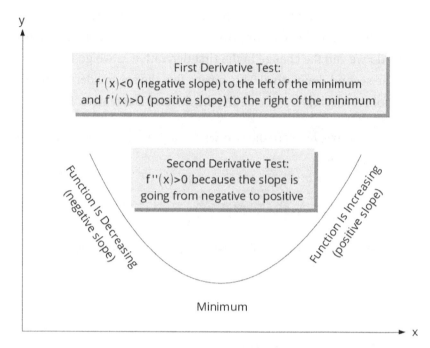

To summarize, here are the two ways you can determine if a critical point is a minimum:

Determining If a Critical Point Is a Minimum

If e is a critical point, then we can determine if e is a minimum in one of two ways:

- **First Derivative Test:** If $f'(x) < 0$ immediately to the left of e and $f'(x) > 0$ immediately to the right of e, then there is a minimum at e.
- **Second Derivative Test:** If $f''(e) > 0$, then there is a minimum at e. This is because the first derivative is going from negative to positive so its change is positive.

And what about the case where there is neither a maximum nor a minimum at the critical point like there was for $f(x) = x^3$?

Determining If a Critical Point Is Neither a Maximum nor a Minimum

If e is a critical point, we can determine that it is neither a maximum nor a minimum in one of two ways:

- If $f'(x) < 0$ immediately to the left of e <u>and</u> immediately to the right of e, then there is neither a maximum nor a minimum at e.
- If $f'(x) > 0$ immediately to the left of e <u>and</u> immediately to the right of e, then there is neither a maximum nor a minimum at e.

When there is a maximum or a minimum the first derivative changes sign. When there is a critical point, but not a maximum or minimum, the first derivative stays the same sign as you go from left to right across the critical point.

To summarize, here are the steps to determine the maxima and minima of a function:

How to Find Maxima and Minima

1. Graph the function to get a visual approximation of where the critical points, maxima, and minima are located. (You can do this at www.CalculusSolution.com/calculus-calculator.)
2. Determine the first and second derivatives. (Again, you can do this at www.CalculusSolution.com/calculus-calculator.)
3. Determine the critical points by finding the values of x where $f'(x) = 0$.
4. For each critical point, apply either the **First Derivative Test** or the **Second Derivative Test** to determine if the critical point is a maximum or a minimum. If the first derivative is the same sign on both sides of the critical point, then there is NOT a maximum or minimum at the critical point.

Exercise: Determine the maxima and minima of:

- $f(x) = x^4 - 10x^3$. (Answer: www.CalculusSolution.com/node/31764.)
- $f(x) = -(x + 7)^2 + 8$. (Answer: www.CalculusSolution.com/node/31765.)

You know everything you need to know about maxima and minima. In the next chapter I'll shift to concavity.

Keep going . . .

Chapter 22 - Concavity (5 minutes)

The concept of **concavity** is best demonstrated with a picture:

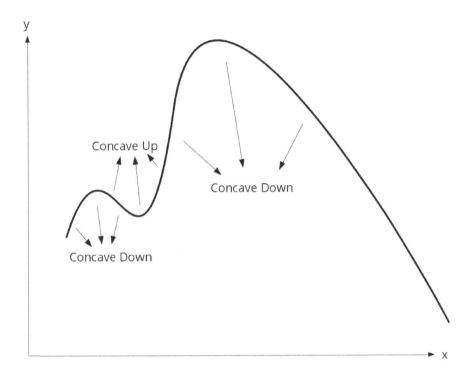

In the picture above, the part of the graph that is **concave up** is like a cup. The part of the graph that is **concave down** is like a cup turned over. We could also say that a function "curves up" when it is concave up and "curves down" when it is concave down.

The concept of concavity is defined in terms of the first derivative:

Concavity

Mathematicians define concave up and concave down as:

- $f(x)$ is **concave up** when $f'(x)$ increases as we move from left to right on the graph.
- $f(x)$ is **concave down** when $f'(x)$ decreases as we move from left to right on the graph.

We can gain some intuition around the formal definition of concavity by looking at specific graphs and getting real numbers. For example, let's look at the function $f(x) = x^2$ whose derivative is $2x$ by the Power Rule. By looking at the graph of $f(x) = x^2$ below, you get the sense (visually) that x^2 is concave up.

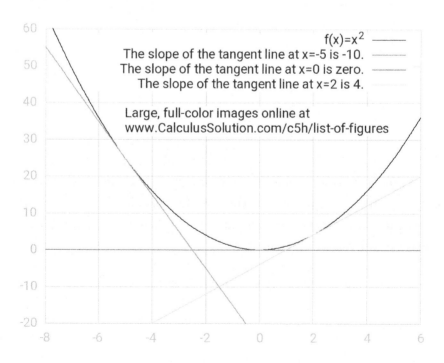

$f(x) = x^2$
The slope of the tangent line at x=-5 is -10.
The slope of the tangent line at x=0 is zero.
The slope of the tangent line at x=2 is 4.

Large, full-color images online at
www.CalculusSolution.com/c5h/list-of-figures

Now let's look at the value of the derivative at -5, 0, and 2. (Note, there's nothing special about these values. I've arbitrarily chosen them.) As the function goes from left to right, $f'(x)$ is getting bigger (-10 to 0 to 4). Since the derivative is increasing x^2 is concave up.

The function $f(x) = x^2$ is an excellent example of a function having the same concavity everywhere. But a function's concavity can change as you move along the x-axis.

A good example of this is $f(x) = x^3$. It's **concave down** when x is negative and **concave up** when x is positive. See the graph of $f(x) = x^3$ below.

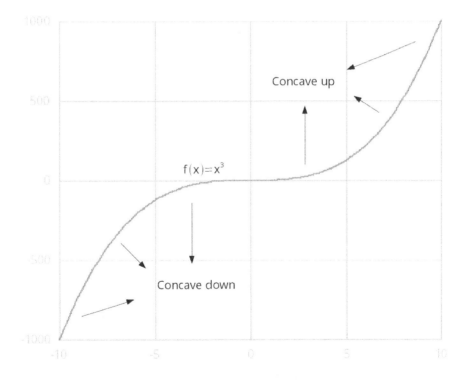

Concavity is an easy concept to grasp, but how do you know the concavity of an entire function? After all, you can't graph it from negative infinity to positive infinity. Keep reading, and I'll show you how to do it.

Chapter 23 - Using Second Derivatives to Determine Concavity (6 minutes)

Remember, concavity is defined as how the first derivative changes as you go from left to right on the graph.

One simple way to determine concavity is with the second derivative. Recall that the second derivative is the amount of change in the first derivative as you go from left to right. This is the *exact* definition of concavity in the previous chapter!

Using Second Derivatives to Determine Concavity

- **Concave Up:** $f''(x) > 0$
- **Concave Down:** $f''(x) < 0$

Let's do two quick examples.

First, in the previous chapter I talked about how $f(x) = x^2$ is always concave up. We know that $f''(x) = 2$, which is always positive. So using the second derivative to determine the concavity worked for $f(x) = x^2$.

It's important to note that I've *proven* it's always concave up. Since you can't graph x^2 over the *infinite* domain of the x-axis, you can <u>never</u> prove it's always concave up by graphing it. The only way to prove it is with the second derivative like I just did.

Second, in the previous chapter we looked at $f(x) = x^3$ and visually observed it's concave down when x is negative and concave up when x is positive. Let's use the second derivative to prove it.

We know that $f''(x) = 6x$ for $f(x) = x^3$. When x is negative, $f''(x) < 0$. (A negative x and a positive 6 always multiply to give a negative number. For example, at $x = -2$, $f''(-2) = -12$.) By showing that $f''(x)$ is negative when x is negative, we've shown that $f(x) = x^3$ is concave down when x is negative.

When x is positive, $f''(x) > 0$. (A positive x and a positive 6 always multiply to give a positive number. For example, at $x = 3$, $f''(3) = +18$.) By showing that $f''(x)$ is positive when x is positive, we've shown that $f(x) = x^3$ is concave up when x is positive.

So, using the second derivative to determine concavity for $f(x) = x^3$ worked!

Exercise: Determine the concavity of $f(x) = x^4 - 10x^3$. Or more precisely, find the values of x for which it is concave up and concave down. (Answer: www.CalculusSolution.com/node/31768.)

Now you know about the concavity of a function, but wouldn't it be nice to know where the concavity changes? That's the subject of the next chapter.

Chapter 24 - Inflection Points (8 minutes)

An **inflection point is where a function's concavity changes**. In other words, it's a point on the x-axis where the function can go from being concave up to concave down, or from concave down to concave up. In the picture below there are four inflection points at $e_1, \cdots, e_4$.

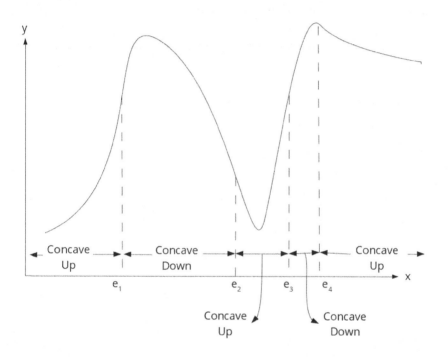

The problem with inflection points is that you can't find them by looking at the graph. For example, you can't look at the graph and know that e_1 is an inflection point. However, there's an easy way to find the inflection points with the second derivative.

In the previous chapter I used the second derivative to determine the concavity. When $f''(x) > 0$ the function is concave up, and when $f''(x) < 0$ the function is concave down. In other words, if e is an inflection point, then $f''(e) = 0$ because the function has gone from positive to negative concavity or negative to positive concavity. This is worth repeating:

The Location of Inflection Points

If e is an inflection point, then $f''(e) = 0$. Inflection points are located at places where the second derivative is equal to zero.

But be very careful with this. Just like a critical point is not guaranteed to be a maximum or minimum, not every point where $f''(x) = 0$ is an inflection point.

To identify a maximum or minimum we first found all the critical points where $f'(x) = 0$. Then we had to look at each one to see whether it was a maximum, minimum, or neither.

Use the same type of thinking here. To identify all the inflection points, first find all the points where $f''(x) = 0$. Then look at each one to see if the concavity changes. If the concavity changes, then it's an inflection point. Otherwise, it's not.

For example, $f(x) = x^4$ has a first derivative of $f'(x) = 4x^3$ and a second derivative of $f''(x) = 12x^2$. The only point where $f''(x) = 12x^2 = 0$ is at $x = 0$. However, $x = 0$ is not an inflection point. Here's why. The second derivative, $f''(x) = 12x^2$, is always positive so the function is always concave up. It's concavity never changes.

So, a place where $f''(x) = 0$ is not guaranteed to have an inflection point. (For $f(x) = x^4$, $x = 0$ is a minimum, and not an inflection point even though $f''(x) = 0$ there.)

Finally, our well known function $f(x) = x^3$ is a great function to demonstrate concavity changes. In Chapter 23 I proved that $f(x) = x^3$ is concave down when x is negative, and it's concave up when x is positive.

Let's use its second derivative to see if we can determine exactly where it changes concavity. An obvious guess is at $x = 0$, but let's prove it.

We know the first and second derivatives of $f(x) = x^3$ are $f'(x) = 3x^2$ and $f''(x) = 6x$. The second derivative is zero at $x = 0$. When x is negative, $f''(x)$ is negative so the function is concave down to the left of $x = 0$. When x is positive, $f''(x)$ is positive so the function is concave up to the right of $x = 0$. This means the concavity has changed as we go from left to right. Therefore, $x = 0$ is an inflection point.

Exercise: Determine the inflection points of $f(x) = x^4 - 10x^3$.
(Answer: See www.CalculusSolution.com/node/31770.)

<hr>

Congratulations, you've made it past all the derivatives stuff! Part 4 is the last big section, and it's all about integrals. Personally, I think integrals are easier. There are less rules, and they're intuitive to learn. Plus, there's a cool surprise in integrals that makes them easy to solve.

Part 4 - Integrals (67 minutes)

In this part you'll learn about integrals - what they are, how to calculate them, and a useful application. I've always liked integrals more than derivatives. They're easier and more intuitive in my opinion.

Let's begin . . .

Chapter 25 - Understanding Integrals (11 minutes)

As you learned in Chapter 4, an integral is a fancy name for the area under the function $f(x)$ between points a and b. It's denoted by

$$\text{Area between } a \text{ and } b = \int_a^b f(x)\, dx.$$

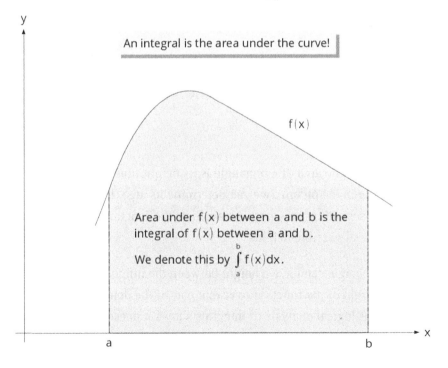

An integral is the area under the curve!

f(x)

Area under f(x) between a and b is the integral of f(x) between a and b.

We denote this by $\int_a^b f(x)dx.$

So how do you determine the area under $f(x)$ between points a and b?

The most common way is to approximate the area with a bunch of rectangles. See the picture below.

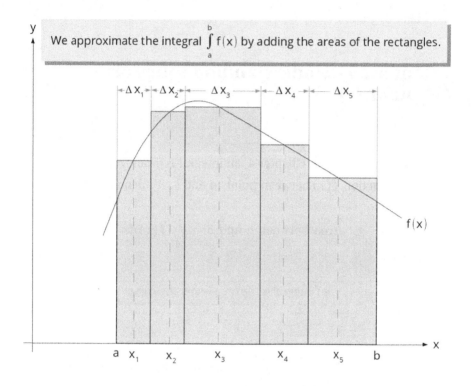

We approximate the integral $\int_a^b f(x)$ by adding the areas of the rectangles.

Remember, the area of a rectangle is its height times its width. For each rectangle in the picture, we can determine its area. Each rectangle has a width. But depending on where we evaluate the function, each rectangle can have several possible heights.

Each rectangle can have a height between the minimum and maximum height of the function over that part of the domain where the rectangle is. A logical analysis of integrals shows it doesn't matter which height you choose. Pick one and use it. Now add the areas of the rectangles to get an *approximate* value of the integral. Again, see the picture above.

Through a complicated process, mathematicians make the width of each rectangle smaller while, at the same time, adding more rectangles. Doing this gives increasingly better approximations of the integral. They continue doing this until they have an infinite number of rectangles with infinitesimally small widths. In other words,

$$\begin{aligned} \text{Integral} \quad = \quad & \text{(Height of } \infty \text{ number of rectangles)} \\ \times \quad & \text{(Width of each rectangle} \rightarrow 0 \text{)} . \end{aligned}$$

As the number of rectangles becomes larger, the integral will become larger. However, the rectangles have a smaller area because their width is getting smaller. This will cause the integral to get smaller.

The difficulty in Integral Calculus is figuring out whether the integral is infinite, zero or somewhere in-between. For most functions that describe the real world, there's a sweet spot in this tug of war between infinity and zero that results in an actual area you can calculate.

Exactly how you go from this concept of adding areas of small rectangles to an exact area is beyond the scope of learning Calculus in five hours. However, this concept does explain where the integration symbol, $\int$, comes from. If you take the S in the word "Summation" (for summation of the area of many rectangles) and stretch it out, you get $\int$. In other words, our symbol comes from

$$\text{Elongated } S = \int .$$

Finally, there are two types of integrals: definite and indefinite. A **definite integral** is the area between two specific points on the x-axis. You usually see the two points labeled a and b where $a < b$.

We refer to a as the **lower limit of integration**, b as the **upper limit of integration**, and both of them collectively as the **limits of integration**.

An **indefinite integral** is an integral that doesn't specify where on the x-axis the area is to be calculated. It results in a formula you can use later to find the area between two specific points, a and b.

Integral	Notation	Gives Us
Definite Integral	$\int_a^b f(x)\,dx$	An actual number that is the area between a and b.
Indefinite Integral	$\int f(x)\,dx$	A formula you can use later to determine the area between two specific points.

Exercise: Use the integral notation to write the following:

- The indefinite integral of $f(x) = x^2 + 5$. (Answer: See www.CalculusSolution.com/node/31772.)
- The area of $f(x) = 5x^3 - 18x^2 - 10$ between -1 and 3. (Answer: See www.CalculusSolution.com/node/31773.)

OK, integrals are just areas, and I've mentioned that finding them is "a complicated mathematical process." You may be wondering, "Is there an easy way to calculate integrals that doesn't require a degree in mathematics?" There is, and it's really cool. But first you need to know what an antiderivative is.

Turn the page now to find out how easy antiderivatives are.

Chapter 26 - Antiderivatives (20 minutes)

Before I show you how to calculate an integral, I need to show you how to calculate an **antiderivative**. This won't make sense until the next chapter, but fortunately, antiderivatives are easy.

Here's the main thing to keep in your head: **A function's antiderivative is another function (let's call it $F(x)$) such that** $F'(x) = f(x)$.

To find a function's antiderivative, do the opposite of what you have to do to find its derivative.

Let's do a quick example.

Let's say that $f(x) = x^3$. What is its antiderivative? Well, do the opposite of what you would have done to find its derivative.

Recall the Power Rule for finding the derivative of x^n. The steps are to multiply the exponent (n) by x^n, and then subtract 1 from n in the exponent. To get the antiderivative, *go backwards*. First, add one to the exponent. Then take the *new* exponent, and divide the function by it. In other words,

$$F(x) = \frac{1}{n+1}x^{n+1}.$$

You can check if this is correct by finding $F'(x)$ and seeing if it's equal to $f(x)$. So, find the derivative of $F(x)$:

$$
\begin{aligned}
F'(x) &= \frac{d}{dx}\left(\frac{1}{n+1}x^{n+1}\right) \\
&= \frac{n+1}{n+1}x^{n+1-1} \\
&= x^n \\
&= f(x).
\end{aligned}
$$

It worked! $F'(x) = f(x)$, so we know our formula for the antiderivative is correct. Now we can answer the question. The antiderivative of $f(x) = x^3$ is

$$F(x) = \frac{1}{4}x^4.$$

Here's the second most important thing you need to know about antiderivatives. What if the antiderivative of $f(x) = x^3$ is the function $G(x) = x^4/4 + C$ where C is some constant number? Because of rules one and two in Chapter 6, we know that $G'(x) = f(x)$. So which is the correct antiderivative of $f(x)$? Is it $F(x) = x^4/4$ or $G(x) = x^4/4 + C$? The answer is that there isn't one antiderivative of $f(x)$. *There are an infinite number of antiderivatives of $f(x)$, and they all differ from each other by a constant number.*

For example, $H(x) = x^4/4 + 18.5$ and $J(x) = x^4/4 - 32.68$ are antiderivatives of $f(x) = x^3$, and they differ from each other by the constant number 51.18. ($H(x) - J(x) = 51.18$.)

Because of this, we always add a constant to "doing the opposite of the derivative" step above and call *that* the antiderivative. In other words, for $f(x) = x^3$ we have

$$F(x) = \frac{1}{4}x^4 + C,$$

where the C reminds us that the antiderivative is not unique. We call C the **constant of integration** for a reason that will become clear in the next chapter.

So here are the four main rules of antiderivatives:

Antiderivative Rule 1: The Antiderivative of Zero

The antiderivative of zero is any constant number, C, because derivative rule one in Chapter 6 says $dC/dx = 0$. Remember, you can always check if an antiderivative is correct by finding its derivative. If $F'(x) = f(x)$, then you know $F(x)$ is an antiderivative of $f(x)$.

Antiderivative Rule 2: The Antiderivative of $K \cdot f(x)$

Let's assume that K is any constant number. If $f(x)$ has the antiderivative $F(x)$, then the antiderivative of $K \cdot f(x)$ is

$$K \cdot F(x) + C$$

because

$$\frac{d}{dx} (K \cdot F(x) + C)$$
$$= K \cdot F'(x)$$
$$= K \cdot f(x).$$

Antiderivative Rule 3: The Antiderivative of $f(x) + g(x)$

Let's assume that $F(x)$ and $G(x)$ are the antiderivatives of $f(x)$ and $g(x)$, respectively. The antiderivative of $f(x) + g(x)$ is

$$F(x) + G(x) + C$$

because

$$\frac{d}{dx}\left(F(x) + G(x) + C\right)$$
$$= F'(x) + G'(x)$$
$$= f(x) + g(x).$$

Antiderivative Rule 4: The Antiderivative of x^n

We've already discussed this, but let's restate it. The antiderivative of $f(x) = x^n$ is

$$F(x) = \frac{1}{n+1}x^{n+1} + C$$

because

$$F'(x) = \frac{n+1}{n+1}x^{n+1-1} = x^n = f(x).$$

It's extremely important to note that this formula works for n being any integer except -1. When $n = -1$, $x^{-1} = 1/x$, and its antiderivative would be

$$\frac{1}{0}x^0.$$

But $1/0$ is not a number! So you can't use this formula to find the antiderivative of $1/x$. In Chapter 32 I'll reveal what the antiderivative of $1/x$ is.

Okay, just one more rule:

Antiderivative Rule 5: The Antiderivative of a Polynomial

If $f(x)$ is the polynomial

$$a_n x^n + a_{n-1} x^{n-1} + \cdots + a_1 x + a_0,$$

then its antiderivative is

$$
\begin{aligned}
F(x) \;=\; & \frac{a_n}{n+1} x^{n+1} \\
+ \; & \frac{a_{n-1}}{n} x^n \\
+ \; & \\
& \vdots \\
+ \; & \frac{a_1}{2} x^2 \\
+ \; & a_0 x \\
+ \; & C
\end{aligned}
$$

because

$$
\begin{aligned}
F'(x) \;=\; & \frac{a_n (n+1)}{n+1} x^{n+1-1} \\
+ \; & \frac{a_{n-1}\, n}{n} x^{n-1} \\
& \vdots \\
+ \; & \frac{a_1\, 2}{2} x^{2-1} \\
+ \; & a_0 x^{1-1} \\
+ \; & 0 \\
=\; & f(x).
\end{aligned}
$$

Exercise: Determine the antiderivatives of

- $f(x) = x$ (Answer: See www.CalculusSolution.com/node/31783.)
- $f(x) = 2x^2 - x + 15$ (Answer": See http://www.CalculusSolution.com/node/31776.)
- $f(x) = x^4 - 10x^3 + 5000$ (Answer: See www.CalculusSolution.com/node/31777.)
- $f(x) = 1/x^3$ (Answer: See www.CalculusSolution.com/node/31778.)

You may be wondering, "What's the use of this antiderivative stuff?" It turns out that antiderivatives make solving integrals super easy. Read on for one of the most important formulas in Calculus.

Chapter 27 - The Fundamental Theorem of Integral Calculus (17 minutes)

$\mathbf{T}$here are many ways to solve the integral

$$\int_a^b f(x)\, dx.$$

However, there's one technique that's so powerful and important it's called **The Fundamental Theorem of Integral Calculus.**

The Fundamental Theorem of Integral Calculus is the primary method we use to solve integrals. Its importance can't be overstated. Furthermore, it provides an elegant relationship between antiderivatives and integrals. Here it is:

The Fundamental Theorem of Integral Calculus

Given a function $f(x)$ and any one of its antiderivatives, $F(x)$, then

$$\int_a^b f(x)dx = F(b) - F(a)$$

for the **definite integral**, and

$$\int f(x)dx = F(x) + C$$

for the **indefinite integral**. C is called the constant of integration.

Now you know why I presented antiderivatives in the previous chapter. The difficulty in calculating the integral has been reduced to finding the antiderivative. And you know how to do that!

Let's do a quick example. Find the area under $f(x) = x^3$ between 1 and 3. In other words, solve

$$\int_1^3 x^3 \, dx.$$

In the previous chapter we found that the antiderivative of $f(x) = x^3$ is $F(x) = x^4/4 + C$, where C is the constant of integration. Now all we need to do is evaluate $F(3) - F(1)$. Here it is:

$$
\begin{aligned}
\int_1^3 x^3 \, dx &= F(3) - F(1) \\
&= \left(\frac{3^4}{4} + C\right) - \left(\frac{1^4}{4} + C\right) \\
&= \frac{81}{4} + C - \frac{1}{4} - C \\
&= \frac{81 - 1}{4} + C - C \\
&= \frac{80}{4} \\
&= 20
\end{aligned}
$$

Notice how the constant of integration subtracted out. That's why it doesn't matter. It always subtracts from itself and never enters into the value of the definite integral.

When I talked about finding antiderivatives I said that antiderivatives are not unique. There are an infinite number of them, and they all differ from each other by a constant number.

It doesn't matter which antiderivative you use because they all differ by a constant number that will be subtracted out when you find the area. The constant of integration *always* subtracts from itself and never enters into the value of the definite integral.

Exercise: Determine the following integrals:

- $$\int_0^a x \, dx$$

(Answer: See www.CalculusSolution.com/node/31782.)

- $$\int_3^{10} 2x^2 - x + 15 \, dx$$

(Answer: See www.CalculusSolution.com/node/31779.)

- $$\int_0^{10} x^4 - 10x^3 + 5000 \, dx$$

(Answer: See www.CalculusSolution.com/node/31780.)

- $$\int_1^2 \frac{1}{x^3} \, dx$$

(Answer www.CalculusSolution.com/node/31781.)

Next up is a bunch of rules for calculating integrals. They're simple and intuitive, but they still need to be stated since you'll use them a lot.

Onward . . .

Chapter 28 - Rules of Integrals (7 minutes)

When we calculate a definite integral like $\int_0^1 x^2 \, dx$, we get a number that is the area underneath x^2 between 0 and 1. We can always add areas because they're just numbers. In other words, adding two areas like

$$\int_{-1}^3 x^2 \, dx + \int_{10}^{11} 5x^3 \, dx$$

can be done because the result of the two definite integrals is a number, and we know how to add two numbers.

But something cool happens when the limits of integration are the same. For example,

$$\int_0^1 x^2 \, dx + \int_0^1 5x^3 \, dx.$$

is the addition of two integrals with same limits of integration, 0 and 1.

This is the rule:

Rule 1: Adding Integrals

When adding two integrals and their **limits of integration** are the same, you can bring both functions under one integration symbol:

$$\int_a^b f(x) \, dx + \int_a^b g(x) \, dx = \int_a^b f(x) + g(x) \, dx$$

Looking at the previous example we have

$$\int_0^1 x^2\,dx + \int_0^1 5x^3\,dx = \int_0^1 x^2 + 5x^3\,dx.$$

What if we multiply a constant times the integral? Here's the rule:

Rule 2: Multiplying an Integral by a Constant

Let's assume that K is a constant number:

$$K \cdot \int_a^b f(x)\,dx = \int_a^b K \cdot f(x)\,dx$$

From these two rules, and setting $K = -1$, you should feel comfortable that:

Rule 3: Subtracting Integrals

When subtracting two integrals and <u>their **limits of integration**</u> <u>are the same</u>, you can bring both functions under one integration symbol:

$$\int_a^b f(x)\,dx - \int_a^b g(x)\,dx = \int_a^b f(x) - g(x)\,dx$$

Rules 1 through 3 are specific cases of this more general rule:

Rule 4: Linear Combinations of Integrals

Let's assume that H and K are constant numbers, then

$$H \cdot \int_a^b f(x)\,dx + K \cdot \int_a^b g(x)\,dx$$
$$= \int_a^b H \cdot f(x) + K \cdot g(x)\,dx$$

In other words, you only need to memorize this rule.

Finally, when two areas under $f(x)$ touch, we can put both under one integral:

Rule 5: Adding Adjacent Areas

Let's assume that $a < c < b$, then

$$\int_a^c f(x)\,dx + \int_c^b f(x)\,dx = \int_a^b f(x)\,dx$$

This rule says that the area of section 1 plus the area of section 2 is the area of the entire region. See the picture on the next page.

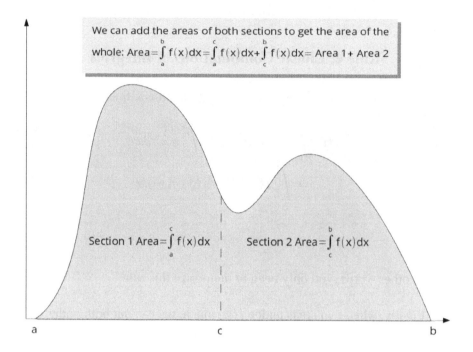

We can add the areas of both sections to get the area of the whole: Area $=\int_a^b f(x)dx = \int_a^c f(x)dx + \int_c^b f(x)dx =$ Area 1 + Area 2

Section 1 Area $=\int_a^c f(x)dx$

Section 2 Area $=\int_c^b f(x)dx$

Exercise: If

$$\int_0^1 f(x)\, dx = 16$$

and

$$\int_0^1 g(x)\, dx = 3.5,$$

then determine

$$\int_0^1 4 \cdot f(x) - 8 \cdot g(x)\, dx.$$

(Answer: See www.CalculusSolution.com/node/31785.)

Integrals can be negative, so I'll talk about why that is in the next chapter.

Chapter 29 - Negative Integrals (5 minutes)

Even though we think of area as a positive number, it's possible for an integral to be negative. There are two things that can make an integral a negative number. First, when the function is negative the integral can be negative:

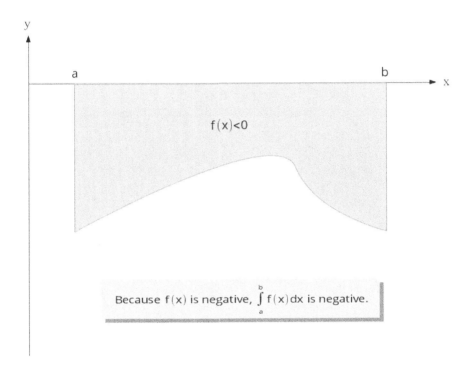

Because $f(x)$ is negative, $\int_a^b f(x)\,dx$ is negative.

In general, you can't immediately tell if an integral will be positive or negative because a function can be both positive and negative between a and b. You have to calculate the integral to know for sure. See the picture on the next page.

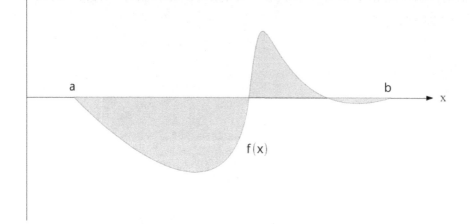

We can't automatically tell if a definite integral will be positive or negative because a function can be both positive and negative between a and b.

f(x)

The second way an integral can become negative is when you change the limits of integration. From the Fundamental Theorem of Integral Calculus we know that

$$\int_a^b f(x)dx = F(b) - F(a).$$

But by the Fundamental Theorem of Integral Calculus we also know that

$$\int_b^a f(x)dx = F(a) - F(b).$$

Notice how I flipped a and b. Now let's do some simple algebra:

$$\int_b^a f(x)dx \;=\; F(a) - F(b)$$
$$=\; -(F(b) - F(a))$$
$$=\; -\int_a^b f(x)dx.$$

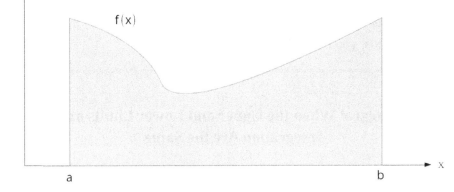

This leads us to an important rule:

Switching Limits of Integration

Switching the limits of integration negates the integral:

$$\int_a^b f(x)dx = -\int_b^a f(x)dx$$

So what is

$$\int_a^a f(x)\,dx?$$

If you think the width is zero so the integral is zero, you're correct. However, there's another way to solve this using the rule above about switching the limits of integration. If $a = b$, then we have

$$\int_a^a f(x)\,dx = -\int_a^a f(x)\,dx.$$

Since the integral is just a number, let's call it N. We have

$$N = \int_a^a f(x)\,dx = -\int_a^a f(x)\,dx = -N.$$

So what is the value of N that satisfies the equation $N = -N$? Zero! Because of this, you now know the following rule:

Integral When the Upper and Lower Limits of Integration Are the Same

For any function $f(x)$,

$$\int_a^a f(x)\,dx = 0$$

You're almost done with integrals! In the next and final chapter on integrals, I'll show you an important application that's simple because you already know how to do it.

Chapter 30 - Using Integrals to Find Average Values (7 minutes)

One of the most important applications of the integral is that of finding an average. In Elementary School you learned the average of a set of numbers is:

$$\text{Average of } n \text{ numbers } a_1 \text{ through } a_n$$

$$= \frac{a_1 + a_2 + \cdots + a_n}{n}.$$

Let's do the same thing for a function. Break the x-axis between a and b into 4 equal width spaces. Now, approximate the average of $f(x)$ like so:

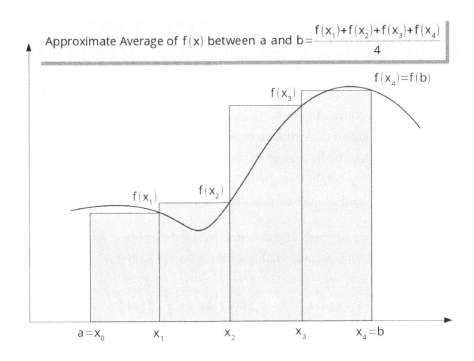

Approximate Average of $f(x)$ between a and b $= \dfrac{f(x_1) + f(x_2) + f(x_3) + f(x_4)}{4}$

In general, you can break the x-axis into n equal width spaces, and approximate the average of $f(x)$ with the equation

$$\text{Approximate Average of } f(x)$$
$$= \frac{f(x_1) + f(x_2) + \cdots + f(x_n)}{n}.$$

Next, multiply and divide by $(b - a)/(b - a) = 1$, and do some algebra:

$$\text{Approximate Average of } f(x)$$
$$= \frac{f(x_1) + f(x_2) + \cdots + f(x_n)}{n}$$
$$= \frac{b - a}{b - a} \cdot \frac{f(x_1) + f(x_2) + \cdots + f(x_n)}{n}$$
$$= \frac{1}{b - a} \cdot [f(x_1) + f(x_2) + \cdots + f(x_n)] \cdot \frac{b - a}{n}$$
$$= \frac{1}{b - a} \cdot [f(x_1) + f(x_2) + \cdots + f(x_n)] \cdot \Delta x$$
$$= \frac{1}{b - a} \cdot [f(x_1) \Delta x + \cdots + f(x_n) \Delta x].$$

In the equation above $\Delta x = (b - a)/n$, and it's the width of each rectangle. The height of each rectangle is the height of the function. For example, $f(x_2)\Delta x$ is the area of the rectangle between x_1 and x_2. Remember, area is height times width. Since the second rectangle has a height of $f(x_2)$ and a width of Δx, the area is $f(x_2)\Delta x$.

To get better and better approximations of the average, add more rectangles with smaller and smaller width. When you do this,

$$f(x_1) \Delta x + \cdots + f(x_n) \Delta x \rightarrow \int_a^b f(x)dx$$

so that

$$\frac{1}{b-a} \quad \cdot \quad [f(x_1)\,\Delta x + \cdots + f(x_n)\,\Delta x]$$

$$\rightarrow \quad \frac{1}{b-a}\int_a^b f(x)dx.$$

This leads to a very important result:

The Average Value of a Function

The average value of $f(x)$ between a and b is

$$\text{Average} = \frac{1}{b-a}\int_a^b f(x)\,dx$$

Exercise: Determine the average value of $f(x) = x^2$ between 0 and 2. (Answer: 4/3. See www.CalculusSolution.com/node/31788.)

OK, you're officially done with integrals, and you have only two more chapters to go. I've presented everything using only polynomials. However, there are two important functions you need to know about. I'll present them, their derivatives, and their integrals.

Oh yeah, and you'll know what the integral of $1/x$ is.

Part 5 - Exponential and Logarithm Functions (12 minutes)

In this last part I'll show you the exponential and natural logarithm functions. The natural logarithm is important because it allows you to integrate $f(x) = 1/x$.

Chapter 31 - The Exponential and Logarithm Functions (7 minutes)

Two of the most important functions in mathematics are the natural logarithm function and the exponential function. These functions are used everywhere in science and math, so being familiar with them is important.

When I initially reviewed functions in Chapter 1, I talked about how a function has a domain, range, and rule that relates an x value to a y value, which is visually represented with a graph. I showed you several functions with their domain, range, and graph. Let's do the same thing here:

Function	Domain (x-axis)	Range (y-axis)
Exponential function: $f(x) = e^x$ or $f(x) = \exp(x)$	All positive and negative numbers	All positive numbers
Natural logarithm: $f(x) = \ln(x)$	All positive numbers greater than zero	All positive and negative numbers

Here's the graph of the exponential function, $f(x) = e^x$:

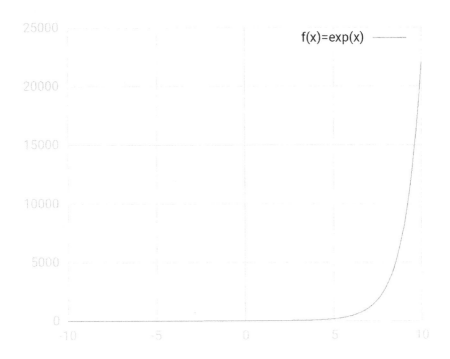

And here's the graph of the logarithm function, $f(x) = \ln(x)$:

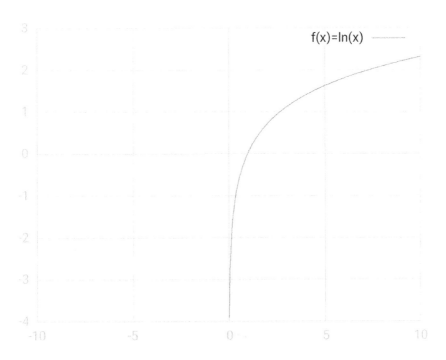

The important thing to note is that the argument for the logarithm function can't be negative. So, for example, $\ln(-2)$ does not exist. Furthermore, neither does $\ln(0)$. As you get closer and closer to zero from the right, the logarithm function becomes more and more negatively large. It goes toward negative infinity.

The logarithm function $f(x) = \ln(x)$ is similar to the logarithm function $f(x) = \log(x)$ you learned about in High School. In general, there's an infinite number of logarithm functions. What distinguishes one logarithm function from another is its **base**. The most generic notation is $\log_b(x)$ which denotes a logarithm function of base b. When you see something like

$$c = \log_b(a),$$

it means

$$b^c = a.$$

For example, $\log_3 9 = 2$.

If this is new to you, think about it this way. When you see $y = \sqrt{x}$ you are really asking the question, "What is the value of y such that $y^2 = x$?" It's the same type of thinking for logarithms. When you see $c = \log_b(a)$ you are asking, "What is the value of c such that $b^c = a$?"

Also, $\log_b(x)$ and b^x are **inverses** of each other. This means

$$\log_b(b^x) = x = b^{\log_b(x)}.$$

When you see $\log(x)$ this means a logarithm of base 10, and when you see $\ln(x)$ this is a logarithm of base $e = 2.7183....$ We call $\log(x) = \log_{10}(x)$ the **common logarithm**, and we call $\ln(x) = \log_e(x)$ the **natural logarithm**.

Because the logarithm functions and their bases are **inverses** of each other, we know that

$$\log(10^x) = x = 10^{\log(x)}$$

and

$$\ln(e^x) = x = e^{\ln(x)}.$$

The natural logarithm function has properties almost identical to those of the common logarithm:

Properties of the Natural Logarithm Function

The numbers a and b are positive numbers greater than zero, and r is any number. The natural logarithm obeys the following:

- $\ln(1) = 0$
- $\ln(e) = 1$
- $\ln(ab) = \ln(a) + \ln(b)$
- $\ln(1/a) = -\ln(a)$
- $\ln(a/b) = \ln(a) - \ln(b)$
- $\ln(a^r) = r\ln(a)$

The exponential function follows the well-known properties of exponents:

Properties of the Exponential Function

- $e^{a+b} = e^a \cdot e^b$
- $e^{-a} = 1/e^a$
- $e^{a-b} = e^a/e^b$

Finally, you may want to check out this blog post:

www.CalculusSolution.com/blog/exponentially-increasing-function

It gives you intuition about the logarithm and exponential functions that is often used in conversations to describe how fast something increases.

You're almost done! On to the final chapter where I reveal the derivatives and integrals of the exponential and logarithm functions. Plus, I'll finally reveal the integral of $1/x$.

Chapter 32 - The Calculus of Exponential and Logarithm Functions (5 minutes)

There are several ways mathematicians develop the Calculus of e^x and $\ln(x)$, but all of them are beyond the scope of learning Calculus in 5 hours. However, just knowing the derivatives of $\exp(x)$ and $\ln(x)$ can give you quite a bit.

The Derivative of $\exp(x)$

$$\frac{d}{dx}e^x = e^x$$

Well, that's easy to remember. The derivative of the exponential function is itself! More importantly, it is its own antiderivative, so from the **Fundamental Theorem of Integral Calculus** we know that:

The Integral of $\exp(x)$

$$\int_a^b e^x \, dx = e^b - e^a$$

Something even more important occurs for the derivative of the natural logarithm function. Here is its derivative:

The Derivative of the Natural Logarithm

$$\frac{d}{dx}\ln(x) = \frac{1}{x}$$

The antiderivative of $1/x$ is $\ln(x)$! This is really important. In Chapter 26, Antiderivative Rule 4 would not allow us to find the antiderivative of $1/x$ because applying the formula made us divide by zero, which we can't do. But now we know its antiderivative and can state that

The Integral of $1/x$ When $x > 0$

$$\int_a^b \frac{1}{x}\, dx = \ln(b) - \ln(a) = \ln\left(\frac{b}{a}\right)$$

Because the domain of the natural logarithm function is all positive numbers greater than zero, the above formula only works for a and b greater than zero. In general, you can have either a and b both greater than zero or both a and b less than zero to get

The Integral of $1/x$

$$\int_a^b \frac{1}{x}\, dx = \ln(|b|) - \ln(|a|)$$

It's important to remember you can't use this formula when a is negative and b is positive. That's because $1/x$ becomes infinitely large as you approach $x = 0$, so the integral becomes infinitely large. Whenever we integrate over a point where the function gets infinitely large we call it an **improper integral**. Calculating improper integrals requires function limits and is beyond the scope of learning Calculus in 5 hours.

With the natural logarithm function and Antiderivative Rule 4, you know the integral of x^n where n is *any* integer and you're not integrating across $x = 0$ for $1/x$.

Finally, we have the integral of $\ln(x)$:

The Integral of the Natural Logarithm

$$\int_a^b \ln(x)\, dx = b\ln(b) - b - a\ln(a) + a$$

where a and b are greater than zero. (There's not too much that's interesting about this, but I thought you would find it strange if I didn't tell you about it when I told you about the integral of $f(x) = e^x$. So here it is in case you're curious.)

Congratulations, you're done! You've made it all the way through, and you should feel proud of how much you've accomplished.

Turn the page now for one last important message about learning Calculus . . .

Need More Calculus Info?

If you've enjoyed this book but want more, point your browser to www.CalculusSolution.com where you'll find lessons, fully worked out solutions to problems, and calculators all designed to make life easier as you learn Calculus.

To get started go to:

www.CalculusSolution.com/Calculus-Starter-Pack

where there's a Calculus starter pack specially designed to get you headed in the right direction. In it you'll find . . .

- The *Calculus In 5 Hours* book in website form with integrated Calculus calculators to make solving the problems easier
- Full and complete access to the CalculusSolution.com website (over 800 pages printed out and counting)
- Four pages of Calculus cheat sheets covering the most important topics
- The guide *How to Make an A+ in Your First Calculus Course*

And all this for *less* than the cost of a McDonald's value meal. So don't wait until things get difficult. Get the tools you need to be successful today. Go now to:

www.CalculusSolution.com/Calculus-Starter-Pack

Glossary

Acceleration: How fast you are speeding up or slowing down. Mathematically, it's the second derivative of the distance-time function. See Chapter 14.

Antiderivative: Given a function $f(x)$, its antiderivative is another function $F(x)$ such that $F'(x) = f(x)$. A function's antiderivative is used in the Fundamental Theorem of Integral Calculus to find integrals quickly and easily. See Chapters 26 and 27.

Area: The amount of 2-dimensional space taken up by an object. Circles, squares, and rectangles are examples of objects that have area. Three dimensional objects can also have area. For example, the surface of a ball is an area. An integral is the area underneath the function $f(x)$.

Average Rate of Change: The amount $f(x)$ changes between two points on the x-axis. See Chapter 13.

Base: What distinguishes one logarithm from another is its base. See Chapter 31.

Brainwashed/brainwashing: The act of believing you're stupid and can't do Calculus despite scientific research that proves you can.

Calculus: Calculus is made up of Differential and Integral Calculus. Differential Calculus is about finding all the slopes a function can have. Integral Calculus is about finding the area underneath a function. See Chapter 4.

CalculusSolution.com: Online website for getting more Calculus information. Go to http://www.CalculusSolution.com.

Chain Rule: A quick way to find the derivative of the composition of two functions. See Chapter 11.

Coefficient: The numbers in front of terms like x^2 in a polynomial. See Chapter 2.

Composition: See *Function Composition* here in the glossary.

Concavity: Denotes the visual perspective of a function looking like a cup or a cup turned over. See Chapters 22 and 23.

Constant of Integration: A variable, usually denoted by C, used to indicate that antiderivatives are not unique. They are subtracted out when the value of a definite integral is found. See Chapters 26 and 27.

Critical Point: : The places on a function where the slope is zero. Maxima and minima reside at critical points, but critical points are not guaranteed to have a maximum or minimum. See also the first and second derivative tests. See Chapters 18 and 20

Decreasing Function: As you move from left to right on the graph, the function will be getting lower. See Chapter 16.

Definite Integral: The area under a function between two points. It's typically denoted by $\int_a^b f(x)dx$. See Chapters 4 and 25.

Degree (of a polynomial): The highest integer n for which a_n isn't zero in the polynomial $f(x) = a_n x^n + a_{n-1} x^{n-1} + \cdots + a_1 x + a_0$. See Chapter 2.

Delta (Greek Δ): Used to denote the difference between two numbers. For example, $\Delta a = a_2 - a_1$. See Chapter 5.

Derivative: The slope of the function $f(x)$ at x. It's denoted by $f'(x)$ or df/dx. See Chapters 4 and 5.

Differential: A really small difference. When Δx becomes really small we call it dx. Similarly, when $\Delta f = f(x_2) - f(x_1)$ becomes really small we call it df. See Chapter 5.

Dimension: The dimension of a number or variable answers the question, "What is this?" See Chapter 12.

Dimensional Analysis: The process of checking to see if the dimension on the left-hand side of an equation is equal to the dimension on the right-hand side. See Chapter 12.

Domain: Where on the x-axis a function is defined. See Chapter 1.

Exponential Function: The function $f(x) = e^x$ (also denoted by $f(x) = \exp(x)$). See Chapter 30.

First Derivative: The slope of the function $f(x)$. It's denoted by $f'(x)$ or df/dx. Also see *derivative* here in the glossary. See Chapters 4 and 5.

First Derivative Test: A method for determining if a critical point is a maximum or a minimum. See Chapter 21.

Function: A mapping of one set of numbers to another. See Chapter 12.

Function Composition: Combining two functions by putting one inside the other. It's denoted by $(f \circ g)(x)$ or $(g \circ f)(x)$. The derivative of a function composition can be quickly found with the Chain Rule. See Chapters 3 and 11.

Fundamental Theorem of Integral Calculus: An important and easy way to find the integral of a function using its antiderivative. See Chapter 27.

Graph: The visual representation of a function's rule that associates numbers on the x-axis with numbers on the y-axis. See Chapter 1.

"ho D hi minus hi D ho over ho ho": A simple way to remember the Quotient Rule. See Chapter 10.

Improper Integral: An integral where the function becomes infinite somewhere between the upper and lower limit of integration, or an integral whose upper or lower limit of integration is infinite. See Chapter 32.

Increasing Function: As you move from left to right on the graph, the function will be getting higher. See Chapter 16.

Indefinite Integral: A formula that can be used to find the definite integral between two points on the x-axis. It's typically denoted by $\int f(x)dx$. See Chapter 25.

Infinity: A word we use to describe something that is bigger than anything else. We denote it by ∞.

Inflection Point: A point where a function's concavity changes. See Chapter 24.

Instantaneous Rate of Change: The amount $f(x)$ changes at a specific point on the x-axis. The instantaneous rate of change of $f(x)$ is its derivative $f'(x)$. See Chapter 13.

Integer: A number like 1, 15, or -182. Numbers like 3.2 are not integers.

Integral: The area underneath a curve. There are two types of integrals. Definite and indefinite. The definite integral is a number that represents the area between two points. An indefinite integral is a formula you can use later to find the area between two points. See Chapter 25.

Integration: The act of solving an integral.

Interval: All the numbers between two other numbers. There are three types of intervals: open, closed, and mixed. Open intervals are denoted by (a, b) and are all the numbers between a and b, but not a and b themselves. A closed interval is denoted by $[a, b]$ and is all the numbers between a and b *including* the numbers a and b themselves. Mixed intervals are a combination of open and closed intervals. Intervals are used to denote things like the domain and range of a function.

Inverses (function): A function's inverse is denoted by $f^{-1}(x)$ and is a function such that the function compositions equal x. i.e. $f(f^{-1}(x)) = x = f^{-1}(f(x))$. In the official math notation we write

$(f \circ f^{-1})(x) = x = (f^{-1} \circ f)(x)$. The natural logarithm and the exponential functions are inverses of each other. See Chapter 31.

Limit (function): A logical process of making one variable slide closer and closer to another variable or number in a function. See Chapter 5.

Limits of Integration: The two points on the x-axis between which you want to find the area underneath a function. See Chapter 25.

Logarithm Function: The function $f(x) = \ln(x)$. See Chapter 30.

Lower Limit of Integration: a in the integral $\int_a^b f(x)dx$. See Chapter 25.

Maxima: Plural of maximum.

Maximum: The part of a function that looks like the top of a hill. See Chapters 19, 20, and 21.

Mean-Value Theorem: The property of a function where the slope of a secant line drawn between any two points will be identical to the derivative somewhere between those two points. See Chapter 15.

Minima: Plural of minimum.

Minimum: The part of a function that looks like the bottom of a valley. See Chapters 19, 20, and 21.

Polynomial: A function of the form $f(x) = a_n x^n + a_{n-1} x^{n-1} + \cdots + a_1 x + a_0$. Straight lines are polynomials. See Chapter 2.

Power Rule: A rule for finding the derivative of x^n. If $f(x) = x^n$ then $f'(x) = nx^{n-1}$. See Rule 4 in Chapter 6.

Product Rule: A quick and easy way to find the derivative of the product of two functions. See Chapter 9.

Psycho: Signing up for an 8:00 a.m. Calculus II class in college.

Quotient Rule: A quick and easy way to find the derivative of the division of two functions. See Chapter 10.

Range: Where on the y-axis a function is defined. See Chapter 1.

Rate of Change: How much something changes with respect to something else. See Chapter 13.

Rectangle: A geometric shape used to approximate an integral. Its area is its width times its height. See Chapter 25.

Rise: How much a straight line goes up per some amount it runs. It's the numerator of a straight line's slope. See Chapters 2 and 5.

Run: The denominator of a straight line's slope. See Chapters 2 and 5.

Secant: A straight line between two points on a function. The secant line's slope is the average rate of change of the function between those two points. See Chapters 5 and 13.

Second Derivative: The derivative of the first derivative. It has several uses:

- Show how much a function's derivative is increasing or decreasing. See Chapter 14.
- Concavity is defined by the second derivative. See Chapter 23.
- Describing the physical act of acceleration. See Chapter 14.
- Identifying maxima and minima of a function. See the *Second Derivative Test* below and Chapter 21.

Second Derivative Test: A method for determining if a critical point is a maximum or a minimum. See Chapter 21.

Slope: A measure of how much a line rises divided by how much it runs. See Chapter 2.

Speed: How much distance you travel per some amount of time. It's the first derivative of the distance-time function. See Chapter 13.

Steep: The amount of slope of a straight line. A slope of six is more steep than a slope of two. A slope of -6 is more steep than a slope of -2.

Straight Line: A function of the form $f(x) = mx + b$ where m is the slope and b is the y-intercept. See Chapter 2.

Tangent Line: A straight line whose slope is the value of a function's derivative at a specific point. See Chapters 5 and 7.

Union: The act of taking all the elements of two sets and putting them together. It's denoted by $\cup$.

Unit: See *dimension* here in the glossary and Chapter 12.

Upper Limit of Integration: b in the integral $\int_a^b f(x)dx$. See Chapter 25.

List of Figures

See **www.CalculusSolution.com/c5h/list-of-figures** for full-color images.

Chapter 13 - Attaching Real World Meaning to Derivatives

- Graphical Intuition of Distance, Slope, and Speed

Chapter 14 - Second Derivatives

- The Change in Positive Slope When the Second Derivative is Positive
- The Change in Positive Slope When the Second Derivative is Negative
- The Change in Negative Slope When the Second Derivative is Positive
- The Change in Negative Slope When the Second Derivative is Negative

Chapter 15 - The Mean-Value Theorem

- The Mean-Value Theorem

Chapter 16 - Increasing and Decreasing Functions

- Definition of an Increasing Function
- Definition of an Decreasing Function
- Function That is Both Increasing and Decreasing

Chapter 17 - Using Derivatives to Find Where a Function Increases and Decreases

- Increasing Straight Line Slope
- Decreasing Straight Line Slope
- Increasing Function With Increasing Secant Line
- Increasing and Decreasing Function With Increasing Secant Line
- Derivative of Increasing Function
- Comparison of Slope and Secant Line of Increasing and Decreasing Function

Chapter 18 - Critical Points

- Critical Points of $f(x) = x^4 - 10x^3$

Chapter 19 - Maxima and Minima

- Maxima and Minima

Chapter 20 - The Relationship Between Maxima, Minima, and Critical Points

- Critical Point, Maximum, and Slope
- Critical Point, Minimum, and Slope
- $f(x) = x^3$ Where the Critical Point is Neither a Maximum nor a Minimum

Chapter 21 - Using Derivatives to Find Maxima and Minima

- Using the First and Second Derivative Tests to Find a Maximum
- Using the First and Second Derivative Tests to Find a Minimum

Chapter 22 - Concavity

- Definition of Concave Up and Concave Down
- Concavity of $f(x) = x^2$
- Concavity of $f(x) = x^3$

Chapter 24 - Inflection Points

- Inflection Points

Chapter 25 - Understanding Integrals

- Integral is the Area Under a Function
- Approximating Integrals with Rectangles

Chapter 28 - Rules of Integrals

- Adding Adjacent Areas:

$$\int_a^c f(x)\,dx + \int_c^b f(x)\,dx = \int_a^b f(x)\,dx$$

Chapter 29 - Negative Integrals

- Negative Integral Because of Negative Function
- Function With Positive and Negative Integral Areas
- Negative Integral Because of Switched Limits of Integration

Chapter 30 - Using Integrals to Find Average Values

- Approximate Average of a Function

Chapter 31 - The Exponential and Logarithm Functions

- Graph of the Exponential Function
- Graph of the Natural Logarithm Function

Made in the USA
Las Vegas, NV
14 August 2023